Wrestling DEPRESSION IS NOT FOR WIMPS!

LESSONS LEARNED FROM AN AMATEUR WRESTLER'S FIGHT TO TRIUMPH OVER DEPRESSION

Chris,
Thanks my fellow scar bearer, for all you do to help others. I'm proud to be your friend.
Skip Mondragón

SKIP MONDRAGÓN M.D.

Wrestling DEPRESSION IS NOT FOR WIMPS!

LESSONS LEARNED FROM AN AMATEUR WRESTLER'S FIGHT TO TRIUMPH OVER DEPRESSION

WRESTLING DEPRESSION IS NOT FOR WIMPS

Lessons Learned from an Amateur Wrestler's Fight to Triumph Over Depression

Christine Kloser's Capucia

Published by:
Capucia, LLC
211 Pauline Drive #513
York, PA 17402
www.capuciapublishing.com

ISBN: ISBN: 978-1-945252-65-5
Library of Congress Control Number: 2019909944

Cover Design: Inspired by Duke Mondragón and in cooperation with Ranilo Cabo
Layout and Typesetting: Ranilo Cabo
Editor: Julie Clayton
Proofreader: Julie Clayton
Book Midwife: Carrie Jareed

Printed in the United States of America

Contents

Dedication

To my three greatest heroes: My little grandma, Audelia M. Anaya, my "abuelita," one of the wisest, faith-filled, and forgiving women I've ever known. You were the hub, steadiness, and calm who kept our family together during the chaos and storm of my early years. My mom, Esther M. Luben, my "Mother Dear," the most courageous, fun, and determined woman I have in my life. Thank you for never losing heart, making a new life for us, and always saying, "Son, reach for the stars. You continue to bring color and delight into my life. My stepfather, Edward L. Luben, my "Daddyo," the most generous, kind, and loving man, I've known. Thanks for opening up whole new worlds to me, and modeling manhood and fatherhood.

To my tough-as-nails Army wife, Sharon J. Mondragón, a.k.a. Sherry, my lover, best friend, confidante, mother of my children, fellow grandparent, fellow word-nerd and author, and co-traveler in this journey of life. Thanks for standing with me throughout our journey during medical school, raising five children, "holding down the fort" while I was deployed for thirty-seven months, including those harrowing and uncertain thirty months in combat zones. You have always been by #1 Fan.

You see me through the eyes of love and stood resolutely by me in my darkest days. You continue to stand by me, support my endeavors, and allow me the time to indulge in my love of wrestling, sometimes for hours on end. *Mi querida,* you are the best!

Foreword

As Skip's youngest brother I can say I have had a front row seat a good part of his life. We share an intimate relationship that goes beyond our family ties: our faith, love of wrestling, and quietly shared successes and setbacks.

In wrestling we develop go-to moves. "Go-to moves" are techniques and strategies that you have practiced over and over again and feel like you have mastered them, so you can trust them and "go-to" them to beat your opponent.

However, no matter how much you practice and train, sometimes there is an opponent who can stop you and your "go-to moves." Skip's "go-to moves" in life are hard work, persistence, determination, and faith. These had worked well, until he confronted an opponent he could not out-work! As a matter of fact, trying to work harder just pushed him down more.

Seeing the self-doubt, even the questioning of his faith, was painful to watch. Skip was knocked on his back by depression, struggled ferociously, but he could not get off his back until he recognized his crafty opponent.

Self-sufficiency has always been part of that "go-to" arsenal that worked in the past...but when does that become a hindrance? Getting off his back required new coaching, help from his teammates, a renewed faith, and an acceptance that he can't just "push through" to defeat *this* opponent.

Enjoy the read, and if you are someone who needs help with depression...please get it!

Chris Mondragón
June 24, 2017

Introduction

I discovered wrestling as a 13-year-old junior high student. Not the highly theatrical and closely choreographed professional wrestling, but the world's oldest and greatest sport, amateur wrestling. Wrestling dramatically changed my life and taught me many valuable life lessons that I have drawn upon since then. In my wrestling career, which spanned over five decades, I lost and won against many worthy opponents. But the fiercest opponent I ever faced was *depression*. This book will tell you how I faced, grappled with, and triumphed over this relentless foe, and how you can too.

As a child, I was typically the smallest boy in my class. To make matters worse, I was shy, socially awkward, and inept at any sport I attempted. I was a regular target for bullies. In the 4th grade, our teacher would take the whole class out to the playground at regular intervals to test the class: chin-ups for boys and bent arm hang for girls. I dreaded when my name was called. I would jump up to the lowest bar, grunt, kick, and pull, but to no avail. I could not do even one chin-up.

Choosing teams during recess was another lesson in humiliation. Invariably, I was the last one chosen and then a chorus would sound, "Awww, why does he have to be on our team?" I was small, weak, slow, and did not know how to run or jump well, much less how to catch, throw, or kick a ball. When I was exposed to wrestling it was the first time I ever had the sense, "I can do this. I think I could be good at this." A lifelong passion for wrestling, something I might be good at, was sparked within this scrawny, clumsy, 13-year-old 8th grader. I soon learned that wrestling pushes you to your limits and taxes you unlike any other sport. Many exceptional athletes that excel at other sports feel humiliated on the wrestling mats, because they're not tough enough for the grueling sport of wrestling. I had this deep inner sense that in spite of being weak, clumsy, and inept at any prior physical endeavors, I could and would succeed at wrestling. Soon I learned I was tough, and had "guts" and tenacity.

I recall the end of the first match I ever wrestled in 1968. I almost crawled off the mat. My head pounded, my lungs burned, my muscles ached, and to make matters worse I was nauseated and my forearms kept cramping up. Fast-forward to 2005, when my son, Jonathan, finished his first match, saying, "Dad, Dad, I think I am going to be sick. I don't think I can wrestle another match." He described the same symptoms I experienced thirty-six years earlier. Unlike me, Jonathan was a fine athlete, a talented and accomplished gymnast, yet he was "welcomed" to wrestling. This painful and indelible experience of the first match is the rite of passage for wrestlers, and has been for millennia.

The physical sensations of headache, nausea, burning lungs, aching muscles and cramping forearms are the initiation into the brotherhood of wrestling. Wrestlers are an unsung group of hard-core athletes who push themselves to their limits, and often beyond what they think their limits are, day in and day out. Training requires discipline, sacrifice, determination, and mental toughness. Does it get easier? Yes, and no. One's body adapts to the rigorous demands, but the best wrestlers continue to push this bar to higher levels. Mental toughness to endure the rigors of practice and competition also requires Herculean effort.

Whether you are a champion wrestler or a mediocre competitor at best, wrestlers respect one another. We understand the rigorous demands of wrestling. When coaching young wrestlers, I warn them, "Wrestling is not for wimps!" It's true; wrestling is not for the fainthearted.

My own journey, which I began as an 8th grader in 1968, was not a cakewalk. I was on the varsity team as the 85-pounder. Alas, I failed to win even one match that year. The good news was that bullies never bothered me again after I began wrestling. The next year, I was the varsity 95-pounder but did not have one win to show for it. The summer before 10th grade, I wrestled in a state freestyle (one of the two Olympic styles) tournament and won, defeating the defending champion. This fueled my love and appreciation of the wondrous sport of wrestling and for wrestlers.

I went on to win many state freestyle tournaments during high school, placed in national freestyle tournaments, and was selected as a High School Honorable Mention All-American. Later, I also went on to win state and regional freestyle tournaments. I am from a wrestling family. My four younger brothers wrestled, my four sons all wrestled, and my father-in-law was an accomplished high school and college wrestler. Two of my most enduring friendships are teammates from high school and summer wrestling. I followed my sons' wrestling closely, coached through the years, won a National Veterans Freestyle Championship in 2012 at the age of 56, and was the National runner-up in 2013. I am also an avid fan. In fact, my kids describe me as a "wrestling groupie."

Wrestling is in my blood and in my family's. Lessons of perseverance, sacrifice, enduring pain and suffering, dealing with failure, celebrating success, and overcoming various injuries are some of the lessons wrestling taught me. Wrestling is one-on-one, face-to-face, hand-to-hand combat. You must overcome the fear of your opponent, the fear of failure, and the fear of public humiliation. My youngest brother Chris, an All-American wrestler at North Carolina State likes to say, "Life will knock you on your back and wrestling teaches you to get up off your back."

In 2014 I was in the match of my life, but this time it was not on the wrestling mat. I grappled with a relentless, merciless, and indefatigable foe. My head was in a fog, my body fatigued, my confidence shattered, my *joie de vivre* (joy of life) was gone,

Inauspicious beginnings. Everitt Junior High School, 1968. I'm the only 8th grader on the varsity squad, first row, far left. My beloved coach, John Gregerson, is in the last row, far left. Our varsity squad had four future Wheat Ridge High School State medalists: one champion, two runners-up (including yours truly), and another placing fourth. It would take Skip two years before he notched his first win.

my optimism evaporated, and I felt utterly alone. *Depression* had knocked me on my back and I was struggling to get up.

In the following pages, I share my fight to free myself from the powerful clutches of a deep, dark despair. I incorporate wrestling stories and the life lessons wrestling taught me, and provide practical tips, tactics, and techniques to aid those who struggle with depression, and to enlighten and assist those who have a friend, colleague, or family member in the grip of depression. Although bruised and bloodied, with the help of professionals, family, friends, and God, I have been victorious over depression.

This book is a labor of love to give hope, help, and encouragement to fellow sufferers who wrestle with depression. I won, and you can too!

CHAPTER I

I Need Help

April 17, 2014, I hit rock bottom. I could no longer compensate and cope. After months of struggling with depression I felt beaten. I will never forget that eventful day when I lay curled up behind the desk in my office, the shades drawn, door locked, and the lights, phone, and pager turned off. I repeatedly asked myself, "Skip, what are you doing?" I did not want to deal with any problems related to patients, subordinates, or the hospital. How did I get to this point?

What happened? After all, I was a twenty-five-year Army Medical Corps veteran, a Colonel, chief of my department, an accomplished clinician, and a recognized teacher. During four deployments, including thirty months in war zones, I experienced personal growth, especially as the Officer-in-Charge of the 21st Combat Support Hospital during Operation Iraqi Freedom I, in 2003–2004. I had the loving support of my wife of thirty-three years, family, close friends, and church. I also had a lifetime of established practices to enhance my resilience. Many of these were born out of my years in wrestling: regular exercise, healthy eating habits, stress reduction, relaxation techniques, visualization, recovering from defeat, tenacity, determination, sacrifice, a willingness to learn, and being coachable. Lying behind my desk in the fetal position, I kept turning my predicament over in my mind, "Skip, what are you doing?" and, "How did I get here?"

After several hours, I finally began to put some of the pieces together. Perhaps the most glaring and disruptive change I could pinpoint was that during the previous nine months I had been experiencing severe insomnia. Most nights I lay in bed for hours longing for sleep. Other nights, after lying in bed for twenty to thirty minutes, I would get up drink some warm milk or herbal tea, read, and then when I felt tired again, return to bed. Alas, my mind would start racing, thinking about work, family, and career issues. I fretted about equipment issues in the Cardiac Catheterization Lab that limited patient care and impacted resident and student training, worried about the decisions and behavior of some of my children, and grew increasingly anxious over employment after I retired from the Army. I would repeat this process of arising and occupying myself until I was sleepy before returning to bed, two, three, and even six or more times a night. On the rare night I easily fell asleep, I would often awaken after two to four hours of sleep, fully awake and unable to go back to sleep. I began to dread nighttime, because I longed for sleep and it had become so elusive.

My usual confidence was replaced by discouraging, self-disparaging, and defeated thoughts. Recurrent thoughts such as, "You failed your family and department" and "Your Army career has not amounted to anything!" plagued me. "You are a failure." "You don't deserve to be a Colonel." "You're a fake!" These were the thoughts playing over and over in my mind that hounded me day and night. This downward spiral of insomnia and incessant self-accusatory cogitations sucked me into a downward vortex. In turn, I was struggling with a crisis of confidence. Day-by-day I grappled with an increasing sense of failure and sleep deprivation, fertile ground for a blue mood.

An optimist by nature, I became sad, despondent, and found little pleasure in my favorite activities. My world became progressively gray, bleak, and bland. Even amateur wrestling—one of the great pursuits of my life—lost its luster. I no longer enjoyed even watching or coaching wrestling, two of my greatest passions.

My libido was diminished too, and I didn't know how to improve it. The emotional and physical energy to be amorous with my wife ebbed. At times, lovemaking was simply too much work. My wife and I had enjoyed a loving, affectionate, and supportive marriage. My diminished libido reflected the increasing self-absorption I struggled to dispel.

A caregiver by nature, I had spent my life looking for opportunities to serve others—serving and caring for others is part and parcel of who I am. Sincere service is profoundly satisfying and fulfilling, and opportunities abounded in my day-to-day activities. I was troubled that I now lacked the inner resources to reach out and respond to the needs of others. My world was shrinking.

In the summer of 2013, a year prior to reaching this turning point while lying on my office floor, I began noticing problems with my cognition. Routinely I could not recall names, find words, or remember what I read. I felt foolish when mid-sentence I could not find the word I wanted to say. It was as though I was unable to locate the files with this information and my mind was darting around, anxiously seeking where it was stored. My brain was in a fog. The fear of early-onset dementia prompted me to discuss my concerns with the Chief of Behavioral Health at my hospital. In late October 2013, he arranged for me to undergo a battery of psychometric tests to evaluate my cognition. Test results, thankfully, were normal, albeit, lower than expected in some areas, based on my education and training. My cognitive impairment was chalked up to my poor sleep, stress related to preparations to retire and relocate from Georgia to Texas, uncertainties about future jobs, adjusting to the empty nest, and the impact of other health issues.

Normally I enjoyed time outside, driving with the sunroof on my car open, and derived magnificent pleasure connecting with nature. The wonder of sitting out on my deck enjoying and marveling at the warmth of the sun, beautiful blue skies, and different birds was gone. I closed the shade to my sunroof, rarely sat out on my deck, and regular communes with nature became a rarity.

Just as I withdrew from communing with nature, I also withdrew from others. Going to work, the gym, and church were exhausting and provoked significant anxiety, and I did not have the desire or emotional energy to engage with others.

I struggled to get through the day, only to find myself longing for a peaceful night's sleep, but unable to enjoy more than a few uninterrupted hours on most nights. I found myself turning down invitations to events that I would have normally accepted with enthusiasm. My world was shrinking and I became increasingly inwardly focused. I lacked the interest, motivation, and energy to engage with others. I felt blue and, at the same time, anxious and on edge. The sensation that my heart was trembling was reflected by the obvious trembling of my hands. I feared others would see this trembling and ask me what was going on. My world was drab and lacked the normal luster that I perceived in life. The lens I looked through at the world became murky and, likewise, I felt my mind and life were murky. My *joie de vivre,* was gone. Where had it gone? Would I ever recover it again?

In late December, 2013, I expressed to my wife Sherry that I was physically and emotionally drained. Exhaustion set in on all fronts. It seemed I was dragging myself through the day and each day was a struggle to make it to the end of the day. At bedtime, the powerful foe of insomnia raised its ugly head and with it, the longing for six, then four, and eventually I would have been so grateful for just two hours of sound sleep. I felt like I had wrestled relentless, crafty, and powerful opponents over and over again. I was thoroughly spent. Now, I was on my back and struggling to get back up.

Four months later, while I lay on the floor of my office for hours asking, "Skip, what are you doing?" I finally admitted out loud: "Skip, you're depressed, go get some help."

Yes, I needed a hand up to begin climbing out of the pit I was in. I was depleted physically, emotionally, socially, and spiritually; now I needed to openly ask for help and willingly receive it. This admission was the turning point and the beginning of my recovery.

Accepting the role of a patient, recipient, and "wounded warrior" meant becoming vulnerable and admitting my dreadful sense of failure. Why was it so hard to ask for help? Pride? Self-sufficiency? Fear of what others would think or how they would react to me? The stigma of mental illness? All of this may have played a role. In retrospect, the fact that I couldn't just work harder, "pull myself up by my bootstraps," and overcome this assailant as I had done so many times in my wrestling career was devastating. This strategy of sacrifice, determination, and persistence—the life lessons wrestling taught me—had served me well throughout my life. It was the *modus operandi* I used to fuel my success as a wrestler and in life. Now I had to acknowledge that I was "broken," and that no amount of gut-wrenching sacrifice, dogged determination, or persistence was sufficient to remedy my situation. I had relied on these resources and strategy to outperform others who were more talented than I was in academic, athletic, and professional pursuits. I touted myself as a classic over-achiever. I joked with close friends that I was a late bloomer in most aspects of my life. My internal resources to "dig deep and gut it out" as we say in wrestling, were depleted. I was broken and it hurt.

Like many men, I did not want to admit to myself or to others that I was a wounded warrior in desperate need of assistance to rebuild my fractured life, to promote healing within my inner being. Where to start? I was in a pit, emotionally and physically exhausted, my mind was in a fog, and my confidence and optimism shaken to their core. I was isolated and withdrawn, and longed for joy, peace, and an ever-elusive refreshing night's sleep. Negative thoughts and doubts hounded me. But with the admission that I was depressed and needed help, I opened my heart and mind to begin the long arduous climb out of the deep, dark despair of depression. I now experienced a flicker of hope and wondrous relief that I no longer had to suffer *alone*.

Wrestlers are no strangers to feeling alone in their struggles. Typically, this aloneness occurs during the "grind" of the mid-season, late December to mid-January. The weather is bleak, often it is difficult to make weight week-in and week-out, mental fatigue has set in, it's hard to keep up with the academics, and there's no time for any other outside activities. When despondent wrestlers finally garner the courage to go to their coach and share their dilemma, it's a relief to unburden themselves and a flicker of hope begins to spark into their hearts and minds. They come to understand they are not alone in their struggles. Instead, they have coaches, teammates, team boosters, and family members standing by to help.

With depression, I had hit the bottom. I was spent. I had no further reserves to draw upon. I had become an observer-participant in my struggle. During those hours when I lay curled up on the floor, I could finally see myself more objectively and put the pieces together. I became my own diagnostician and made a mental checklist of what I was experiencing: depressed mood, impaired concentration and memory, anxiety, lack of hope and confidence, insomnia, lack of interest in my passions, decreased libido, overall diminished energy, withdrawal and social isolation, and self-deprecating thoughts. This checklist helped me to finally see and admit I was depressed, and that I needed help. Later, when my mood brightened, I quipped to my family and friends, "If I had been my own doctor, I would've diagnosed my depression long before I was finally diagnosed."

Lessons Learned

Depression is accompanied by:

- A severely blue and darkened mood.
- Shame and guilt
- Impaired cognition.
- Anhedonia (loss of interest in one's passions).
- Lack of energy.
- Self-incriminating and self-deprecating thoughts (negative ruminations).
- Loss of confidence.
- Hopelessness.
- Decreased libido.
- Social withdrawal and isolation.
- Altered and disrupted sleep. (Some sleep excessively and those, like me, might also suffer insomnia and early morning awakenings.)
- A loss of your joy of life *(joie de vivre)* and the hope of recovery.

Asking for Help Can Be the First Step to Recovery

- Don't suffer alone.
- If you are struggling, speak up and ask for help!
- Once you admit you're depressed, don't let the stigma associated with depression keep you from seeking help.
- The admission, "I'm beaten and broken!" is especially difficult for men—it was for me.
- If you are suffering from depression, do not, do not, *do not* let one more day pass without seeking help!
- Once you seek help, you will be seen as courageous, not fearful or weak.
- Those who love you and professionals who will help treat you, all recognize on a deep level that we are all wounded warriors.
- The sooner you ask for help and accept it, the sooner you can begin to heal.
- Those who love and care about you, along with trained professionals will respond with compassion, kindness, and patience, when you ask for help.
- Depression impacts your whole being, body, mind, and spirit—it's essential to address all aspects when recovering from this disease.

CHAPTER 2

Suffering

On that fateful day in April 2014, I decided I would begin to share my doubts, burdens and fears. In doing so, I opened the door to the possibility of recovery and renewal. Yes, I was depressed! Yes, I needed help. I walked down to my Primary Care Provider's clinic and requested the first available appointment with the clinic's clinical psychologist. An appointment was scheduled for the following week. After I returned to my office, I realized I did not want to wait until the following week. I called the Chief of Behavioral Health, explained my situation, and he arranged an appointment with a clinical psychologist for that afternoon.

I arrived at my appointment and met a very kind, gracious, and astute Army Captain. She conducted a thorough intake interview, including an assessment of my risk of suicide or homicide. Before I left, she told me that she and her chief determined I was a good fit to work with another clinical psychologist, Lieutenant Colonel (LTC) Mike Perry. Admitting that I was depressed provided the impetus to seek help, and my first appointment with the psychologist cracked the door to recovery open.

No one wants to suffer. Yet suffering eventually finds us at some point in our life. I tell others that if you have not experienced deep, life-changing suffering, you simply have not experienced enough life. Sooner or later, profound suffering knocks on each of our doors. I had been battered by suffering for ten months before I admitted I was depressed and was formally diagnosed. We can try to ignore suffering, but to no avail. I tried to minimize my suffering. Ignore it. Deny it. Scream at it. Pray it away. Yet it became my constant unwanted companion. Even in the best of moments, it resolutely stood next to me. I could not free myself from its powerful grasp. I was no match for this overpowering foe. Suffering, suffering, suffering!

My body suffered. I was bone tired. Aches and pains from old injuries and osteoarthritis made the suffering of my mind and spirit worse. Pain in my knees, hips, shoulders and other joints made it hard to relax and feel comfortable. I regularly applied ice or heat, used a massage roller, soaked in a hot tub or took a long hot shower, to decrease the pain and limit my use of Tylenol or other pain relievers like Motrin. My body seemed to betray me. I was dedicated to rigorous fitness routines, eating a healthy diet with good portion control, and giving strict attention to adequate sleep.

In the nine months leading up to my admission of being depressed I had undergone three surgeries. In September 2013, I underwent a graft, taking tissue from my hard palate to treat the receding gum of my lower front teeth. The graft went off without a hitch and I had nominal pain afterwards. The hardest part was not being able to brush my teeth for several days or to eat crunchy foods like apples and fresh vegetables, lest I disrupt the graft. Recovery was right on track until I began to bleed profusely from the graft site on my hard palate.

One moment I was fine. Then, without warning or any provocation, I'd feel a warm spurt of blood in my mouth. I'd quickly apply pressure with my thumb and spit out blood for up to forty-five minutes or longer until I could get control of the bleeding. This necessitated a call to my oral surgeon to arrange to be seen expeditiously. This recurred three times, generally late at night or early in the morning. Reluctant to make a trip to the Emergency Room, I would wait until after 6 AM to call. When I returned the third time, my oral surgeon cauterized the graft site and this finally resolved any further bleeding.

During my recovery, I had to avoid any strenuous exercise and had to alter my diet, avoiding favorites such as crunchy fruits, vegetables, and nuts. These are staples in my daily fare. Limiting my exercise made me antsy and impacted the quality of my sleep. My body was accustomed to regular vigorous exercise. For the first several days I was restricted to walking around the house. Then I was allowed to walk at a slow to moderate pace. My oral surgeon warned me against exercises that increased my blood pressure—calisthenics, weight-lifting, skipping rope, sprints on the cross trainer—exercises I enjoyed and regularly engaged in. Not to mention, I absolutely had to refrain from coaching wrestling. Ugh!

Not only did I decondition during my recovery, but my daily routine, nutrition, and sleep were disrupted. It took several weeks to settle back into my normal routine, except for my sleep. The problems of falling and staying asleep that became problematic five months earlier, were now compounded. Trouble falling asleep, or awakening in the middle of the night or early morning and not being able to fall back asleep, became more frequent and more severe. It took me longer to fall asleep, and if I awoke in the middle of the night or early morning hours, it took longer and longer to fall asleep again.

Then, in late November, I experienced severe right knee pain while walking. I altered my workouts, applied ice, and took Tylenol or Motrin, all to no avail. I had to walk at a slow pace and avoid any quick turns. Climbing steps was out of the question. This was frustrating because I rarely rode an elevator, even when I had to visit the thirteenth or fourteenth floors of our hospital. Out of options, and sidelined from activities including coaching wrestling, I sought out the orthopedic surgeon who operated on my shoulder when I returned from Iraq in 2011.

My orthopedic surgeon examined me, ordered x-rays, and explained I needed an MRI, in anticipation of surgery to correct the suspected damage in my knee. I was to limit my activities to those that did not cause pain. Ugh! I reviewed the MRI with my surgeon and he recommended arthroscopic surgery because I had damage and wear and tear in my right knee that physical therapy and time were not going to heal. Once again, my daily routine was disrupted and this negatively impacted my sleep and my mood. We arranged surgery for mid-December, so I could utilize the Christmas and New Year holidays to recover.

Surgery proceeded without any complications. I was at home using my Polar Ice cooler (a machine that circulated ice water through a pad wrapped around my knee) religiously. Likewise, I used crutches, took my pain medication as prescribed, and kept my leg elevated when I wasn't doing range of motion exercises as instructed for my knee. It was hard to get comfortable in bed at night and certain movements caused pain that frequently awakened me. I was also bored and became jittery because of my limited activity.

A few days after surgery the pain heightened and any movement of my leg sent a severe shooting and burning pain into my right thigh. I supplemented my pain medication with additional doses of Motrin. I could not get comfortable. I only slept in short snatches and it was excruciating to get up to use the bathroom or hobble to the kitchen table to eat. I was miserable and tried to distract myself to help deal with the pain. I tried to read, watch TV or movies on NETFLIX, write, pray, and meditate. The pain made it difficult to concentrate on much of anything for more than a few minutes at a time.

I feared I had a deep vein thrombosis (a clot in the deep veins) in my thigh, a relatively common complication of knee surgery. My wife loaded me up in the car and drove me to the Emergency Room. It was torture to hobble out to the car on crutches and to get in and out of the car. The ultrasound ordered by the ER doctor showed that there was no clot. The doctor attributed my pain to excessive exercise and a resultant strain of my thigh. He prescribed a muscle relaxant. After three doses of the medication I was no better.

This prompted a call the next day to my orthopedic surgeon. He was attending a medical conference in Colorado, so it took several hours to return my call. I explained my symptoms and that I was concerned I had a complication called regional pain syndrome. My surgeon concurred and indicated there was no time to lose. Unless regional pain syndrome is treated quickly and aggressively, it can result in chronic, disabling pain. He, in turn, referred me to a Physical Medicine and Rehabilitation specialist, a physiatrist. We arranged for me to see her early the next morning. I spent another fitful and painful night, but hopeful that relief was on the horizon. After completing her evaluation, the physiatrist said, "We are going to hit this hard." A short while later I was in the lobby of the pharmacy awaiting my prescriptions for high doses of morphine and Prednisone. I took a dose of morphine immediately upon receipt of the medications and later took a dose of prednisone.

Twenty-four hours later my pain was greatly reduced. In addition, the low-level headache and nausea that I had experienced for days were gone. My body relaxed for the first time in almost a week. The remainder of my recovery was uneventful, albeit slow. Over the next four to five weeks, I progressed from two crutches, to one crutch, and then a cane. Eventually, I began walking short distances without the cane. All the while, I participated in physical therapy, with gusto, two to three times weekly. Quick movements and rope skipping were out of the question, due to pain, until at least six months after surgery.

Once again, my exercise routine, sleep, and involvement in coaching wrestling were impacted. My deteriorating physical fitness reflected the deterioration in my mood. I was progressively blue, negative thoughts plagued me, and I spent many nearly sleepless nights. I have come to understand that vigorous exercise has been a vehicle to manage my anxiety and the stress in my life. Not to mention that my self-image, in part, was rooted in maintaining a superb level of physical fitness and actively working with young wrestlers during practice. Now these were stripped away from me, and other ways to compensate failed me. For example, I lacked the emotional, mental, or physical energy, along with the inability to quiet my mind and heart, and focus, to pray reflectively, meditate, or journal to help me stay on an even keel.

While I recovered from my knee surgery, I underwent a third surgical procedure, laser facial scar resurfacing in late February 2014. During my recovery, I developed an infection, so my dermatologist prescribed an antibiotic. Unfortunately, after one dose I experienced severe numbness and tingling of my hands and feet, which plagued me for over a year. During my recovery from the laser procedure, my activity was curtailed, including rehab for my knee, and my mood and sleep deteriorated even more.

As a lifelong wrestler, regular and vigorous physical activity has been a mainstay of my daily routine. I feel better, think better, deal with stress better, sleep better, and am calmer when

I exercise regularly. Disruptions to my regular exercise routine contributed to my depressed mood. This recurrent pattern of disrupted activity/exercise, diet, daily routines, and sleep, contributed to my darkened mood. Moreover, my deteriorating fitness and body composition, and the profound impact they had on my confidence and self-image further plunged me deeper into depression. Yes, I suffered in body, but even more so in my mind.

Lessons Learned

- Suffering is inevitable.
- Suffering impacts your whole being—body, mind and spirit.
- Suffering can teach you valuable lessons, if you are a willing pupil.
- Stress is cumulative:
- Stressors, such as illness, surgery, and disrupted routines can deplete stress-reducing and resilience-enhancing habits.
- If stressors occur singularly or at intervals that allow for adequate recovery, their impact can be minimized.
- If not, the additive or cumulative effect can be profound and even devastating.
- Daily exercise, heathy nutrition, and sound sleep are essential to health and well-being.
- Resilience is important to weather the storms of life.
- Resilience is enhanced by regular refreshing sleep, good nutrition, and daily exercise.

CHAPTER 3

Doom and Gloom The Big Three, Plus One

As I just mentioned, the three pillars of good health are regular exercise, a nutritious diet, and adequate and restful sleep (the "BIG 3"). Even the former U.S. Army Surgeon General, Lieutenant General (3-star) Patricia Horoho, has praised the importance of sleep for health and well-being, and I certainly struggled with that one. But what about another critical aspect of well-being that isn't so easy to identify when it's lacking, but is equally detrimental: a healthy mind and positive outlook?

Chapters four, five and six will briefly dive into the "BIG 3" of physical well- being, but first, in this chapter we will take a short ride on the train of mental well-being and notice how we can get hijacked and end up somewhere unfamiliar and undesirable. Or as I call the importance of mental well-being, the "Plus One." No matter where you go, your "plus one" always goes with you.

In the sport of wrestling, wrestlers struggle not to be "psyched out" by the physique, reputation, and body language of their opponents. Positive, confident thoughts not only affect our minds, but our bodies. Negative thoughts translate into negative physiology: our strength, endurance, reaction time, and recovery are all diminished by negative thinking. Conversely, they are improved with positive thinking.

As my depression progressed, I was battling ever more powerful and relentless dark, negative, and self-disparaging contemplations. Negative cogitations exacerbated my insomnia and diminished my ability to cope with my weary, pain-wracked, and deconditioned body. The struggle in my mind grew even more ferocious, and made the suffering in my body even worse. What had happened to my positive, confident, and hopeful self-talk and attitude? Where had they gone?

Negative thoughts plagued me day and night. They were relentless, intruding, like an unwelcome guest, when I prayed, meditated, read, or conversed with others. They were especially unwelcome foes when I went to bed. With the distractions of daytime removed, these negative ponderings loomed larger. It was the same thoughts, the same tapes that looped around over and again: "You don't deserve to be a colonel. You're a failure. Your Army career has not amounted to anything. You're a fake. You don't deserve to be the chief of your department. You've failed your family and your department!" These and other negative accusations played over and over in my mind like a recording that I only could only silence for a brief time. These negative thoughts, or "negative ruminations" as they are called in medical circles, are the unwanted companion of those suffering from depression. Like a cow chewing on its cud, I found myself ruminating on these self-incriminations. I wanted to believe they were false accusers, yet I could not shake their relentless pounding.

I remember sharing these self-disparaging thoughts with my kind, skillful, and compassionate psychologist, Lieutenant Colonel Mike Perry, PhD, who I was seeing each week by this time. Dr. Perry is a tall, distinguished-looking, and highly experienced Army Officer and clinician, who brought a sense of calm into the room with him. In one of our earliest sessions I tearfully shared, "I don't want to end my Army career with a whimper. I envisioned ending it on a strong and confident note." He countered, "You may feel this way now, but let's look at the evidence. Based on your record, I don't think this is true. Have you considered…?" He went on to ask some probing and thought-provoking questions to help me distinguish feelings from facts.

My normal optimism and can-do attitude were not operational. I struggled with insecurities. Not only did I feel like a failure to my family, the Army, Eisenhower Army Medical Center, and the Department of Medicine, my department, but I began to fret about a career after my upcoming retirement from the Army. I worried, "How am I going to take care of my wife and my family? Who is going to want to hire me? What if I don't get better? I can't remember simple things, such as names, medical syndromes I am very familiar with, and what I read five minutes earlier. Who is going to offer me a job? What if I am out of work for an extended time and we deplete our savings?"

This crisis in confidence was like my freshman year at The University of Notre Dame in the fall of 1973. The summer of 1973 was the first summer since starting wrestling that I did not compete in tournaments. Instead, I spent the summer serving first on the work crew of a Young Life Camp (a Christian organization for youth), and later with *Amigos de las Americas* administering DPT (diphtheria-pertussis-tetanus) vaccinations in Guatemala. Bilateral ankle sprains also preempted me from running and rope skipping, and I did not have access to a weight room, so my training was further disrupted. I arrived at Notre Dame in my worst level of wrestling fitness ever.

I trained hard before the start of wrestling season and improved my conditioning significantly. Then I walked into our first practices. My main competitor was bigger, stronger, and more skilled down on the mat. I could not control him for long when I was in the top position and I had trouble getting away from him when I was in the down position. As the weeks wore on, my confidence waned. I showed up every day for practice and worked hard, but each week when we wrestled off, it was more of the same—he defeated me.

Now, forty-one years later, and like my competitor in the Notre Dame wrestling room, I was contending with a larger, more powerful, and more accomplished foe. He had me down on the mat. No matter how hard I struggled, I could not shake him.

Glimmers of hope became less frequent. I began to despair that my life could be better. Guilt added to my despair. I worried that I would not be able to provide for my wife in the manner I envisioned after our retirement from the Army. I also feared that we would deplete savings to pay for our youngest son's college expenses. I felt guilty that I was not more available to my wife, children, and extended family—much less, to friends, colleagues and patients. I progressively withdrew from activities such as coaching wrestling, watching wrestling, or activities outside of work. With my gradual withdrawal, my guilt correspondingly increased. I lacked the emotional energy to remain engaged, except for brief periods. I contended with gloom, doom, and shattered confidence.

Since I constantly contended with these dark accusations in my mind, my mental health professionals regularly assessed my risk for suicide. At each Behavioral Health appointment, I was asked whether I was experiencing suicidal or homicidal thoughts. Suicidal, and far less frequently, homicidal thoughts, can plague individuals who are depressed. In fact, depression is frequently associated with attempted and, all too sadly, completed suicides. I am most grateful that I did not contend with either of these horrible symptoms. If you are dealing with thoughts of suicide, seek help immediately. Go to the nearest E.R. Call 911 or the National Suicide Prevention Lifeline. Don't struggle with suicidal thoughts alone. Stop reading, and go get help, now!

Dr. Perry regularly assured me, "You are going to get better!" He reminded me, "You are not alone." He helped me to see and say, "Yes, I have a loving wife, children, and an extended family supporting me. I also have a supportive and loving church and friends who are standing by to assist me."

Still, my mind was unsettled. When I tried to pray or meditate, the usual despondent and guilty thoughts intruded. My focus and attention were further hampered by a growing sense of doubt, fear, and shame. Prayer, and reading and studying the Bible were laborious. Thoughts bounced around in my mind and it was hard to maintain a train of thought. "What am I going to do? What did I just read?" I experienced a growing sense of dread asking myself, "Am I going to have to struggle with this impaired cognition for the rest of my life?"

Dr. Perry countered my negative thinking with assignments, such as:

1. "Recall and document *three* successes you enjoyed at different stages in your life."
2. "Consider the things you've done over the years to assist others, why you did them, and how this made you feel."
3. "Relive some happy moments and why they are meaningful to you."

He helped me counter *the negative tapes running in my mind,* look at them more objectively, and see how evidence in my life did not support, but, in fact, refuted them.

It was slow going because the failures and sadness in my life loomed very large. It took a concerted effort to reframe these failures in light of the successes and joyous experiences throughout my life. Looking at life through the lens of fear, failure, and fruitlessness sapped my joy and passion. In fact, it was hard to make it through each day because of my limited emotional, mental and physical, energy. Day by day I had to rebuild my outlook and perception of what my life stood for. I began to slowly recover my purpose and my passion. It was a long and painstaking process with many stops, setbacks, and restarts.

If you recall, I wrestled for two years before I ever won a match. With daily sacrifice, discipline, and focus, I graduated as a High School Honorable-Mention All-American. When I wrestled at the University of Notre Dame my confidence took a beating and it showed in my mediocre wrestling record. Later, after I left Notre Dame, I went on to win state and regional freestyle tournaments in 1978. Finally, in 2012 the same daily sacrifice, discipline, and focus helped me to win a National Veterans Championship. I know what it is to face defeat, discouragement, and setbacks on the wrestling mat. Likewise, I've also savored success to master a new move, defeat a tough foe, or win a hard-fought championship. It required daily discipline.

Now I found myself in a struggle with a new devious and powerful foe and was working with all my might to reclaim some confidence in this fight. I had to draw upon the same lessons of daily sacrifice, discipline, and focus. It did not matter how I felt or whether I wanted to do certain things. I pushed myself to do them because I knew they would they would help my recovery. And I was determined to do everything I could to recover.

I resolved that I would make the most of each day. Upon awakening, some days all I could mutter was, "Thank You, Lord." On other days, I might manage to quote, if I could recall it, a Bible verse such as Psalm 103:1: "Bless the LORD oh my soul and all that is within me, bless His holy name." Throughout my journey I was determined to express gratitude. Even when I did not feel like it, I'd say, "I am grateful God loves me, my wife loves me, and so do my children. I enjoy many blessings." In the depths of my depression, I continued to express gratitude, even though my heart was heavy and my mind and body weary. I chose to express thanks, even if haltingly, to God, my wife and family. On many days expressing gratitude was a sheer exercise of my will, because my emotions were enveloped in despair and discouragement. Several years before, I decided that no matter how I felt, I would choose to express gratitude. This practice served me well in my deepest and darkest days. "Thank you," is a powerful antidote to self-preoccupation and self-pity.

The self-absorption and limited physical, mental, and emotional energy imposed by depression troubled me. I am a caretaker by nature, so I enjoy serving others. It was understandable but frustrating for me that during this period I had very little capacity to be supportive or encouraging of others. For example, after the 8–9 AM Morning Report, during which the staff and resident physicians discuss cases admitted the night before, I routinely would visit cancer patients undergoing treatment at Eisenhower Army Medical Center. I enjoyed meeting, chatting, and offering words of encouragement and prayer with patients and their families. But I stopped visiting the Infusion Center. I did not have the emotional and mental energy to engage with patients and their families. Many days I tried to muster the energy to do so, but realized, "I can't do it." It never occurred to me when I was healthy how much mental and emotional energy was required to engage with cancer patients and their families. My regular routine of stopping in for ten to fifteen minutes became an arduous and insurmountable "task." It was no longer an enjoyable labor of love. My inability to reach out added to my guilt and my discouragement. I was a caretaker who now lacked the inner resources to take care of others. Ugh!

At the prompting of Dr. Perry, I made an appointment with my primary care physician. I was comforted and encouraged by her compassion, kindness, and patience. She performed a thorough medical evaluation to ensure I did not have other medical causes related to my depression. After completing her evaluation, she told me, "I don't detect any other medical causes for your depression." (Some of the other diseases associated with depression include thyroid disease, PTSD, chronic pain syndromes, heart disease, diabetes, and substance abuse.) "I think you should start an antidepressant. What do you think?" I agreed, and left with a prescription.

Medication, combined with the skillful treatment of my primary care provider and Dr. Perry, along with the tender loving care of my wife, family, and church helped to kick-start an improved mood. More and more I began to recognize, acknowledge, and enjoy past accomplishments and contributions.

I started to counter the negativity in my mind, albeit, haltingly at first. My mood, confidence, and mentation began to improve, but my sleep remained problematic.

How to Grapple Successfully with Doom and Gloom

Counter Negative Thoughts

Negative thoughts haunt those struggling with depression. It takes concerted effort and a plan to counter these discouraging mental tapes and not become "psyched out" by your powerful, mean, and crafty opponent. You may recall too what I said earlier—that negative thoughts negatively impact our physiology. As the saying goes in wrestling, "If you think you're beat before you start, you're right!" To counter negative thoughts, sometimes described as ANTs (automatic negative thoughts), you must recognize and deal with them. Strategies include:

- Become curious about these thoughts. Instead of trying not to think about them, objectively look at them. Ask yourself, "Is this true? What would it look like if was always true? Or, always false?" Continue to probe and ask, "Is there evidence to support this thought? If not, is there evidence to the contrary?"
- Be on the outlook for "always" and "never" statements. "I always forget names. I can never remember how to do this." Use the same objectivity as above to explore and deal with these types of thoughts.

- Likewise, be aware that "could've, should've, and would've"—regrets—root you to the past, instead of moving you forward. These thoughts often lead to guilt, which is one of the hallmarks of depression.

Overcoming Guilt

Guilt is like wrestling a powerful opponent who frustrates your every move and imposes his will on you. To counter guilt you may wish to employ:

- Forgiveness! Forgive yourself. You are often your harshest critic. (I know I am.)
- Forgive others. If you harbor bitterness, resentment, or unforgiveness, these are poison to your soul and have no place in healing the wounds of depression.
- Share your sense of guilt in detail with trusted family, friends, or professionals such a counselor or clergy member. They can provide more objective feedback.
- Offer heart-felt gratitude for forgiveness from God and from others and enjoy a newfound freedom and, even joy.

Relive Accomplishments

Another tactic to counter negative self-incriminating thoughts is to recall and relive accomplishments. For example:

- List the Top 10 accomplishments during different decades or stages of your life.
- List the Top 100 accomplishments of your life.

- Recount the major successes you enjoyed during the past year.
- Surround yourself with memorabilia that attest to past accomplishments such as diplomas, awards, promotion certificates, trophies, plaques, photos, and letters.
- Wrestlers proudly wear their letter jackets and display medals, trophies, tournament brackets, and photos.
- Those of us in the military wear medals and ribbons, and display military promotion certificates, and military coins.
- Many veterans proudly display their rank and unit insignia, medals, and ribbons, along with a traditionally folded U.S. Flag in a shadow box. This serves as a concrete reminder of their sacrifices, accomplishments, and service to our Nation over the course of their careers.

Positive Declarations

Consider adopting mantras. While training for the Veterans National Freestyle Wrestling Tournaments in 2012 and 2013, I employed mantras during my training. These included, "Strong, fast, tough!" while I pushed my mental and physical capacities in training. I also used, "I am lean and mean," both while training and when saying, "No!" to a variety of tasty treats to slim down to compete in the 58-kilogram (127.6-pound) class. These mantras served me well to achieve my goals. Likewise, I employed mantras to help me contend with my negative ruminations while in the throes of depression:

- "I am a beloved child of God."
- "My family, friends, and church love me."
- "I am kind, generous, and loving."
- "This is the day the Lord has made. I will be glad and rejoice it."
- "I will be kind to myself today."

Patience

- Be patient.
- Depression is an insidious and crafty opponent who sneaks up on you; usually it is only long after you are in its powerful grip that you recognize and admit you need help.
- Skillful and compassionate professionals will help you cope with and counter the negativity in your mind.
- As your depression abates, so will the dark and foreboding cloud in your mind.
- Progress will often come in fits and starts with setbacks along the way—this is normal—accept each day as it comes.

Over the months of treatment, Dr. Mike Perry was instrumental in helping me reframe and reorient my thinking so I understood and appreciated that my Army career did not "end with a whimper." Likewise, in the coming the pages, you will see the many loving, kind, and patient contributions of others to help me in my recovery. I ended my Army career on a high note with a fabulous retirement ceremony and retirement dinner. My family, close friends, and colleagues were present to honor me and to celebrate with me.

Lessons Learned

- Depression is monstrous, powerful, and devious:
  - Don't be "psyched out!"
  - Enlist the help of professionals and loved ones to help you in the fight.
- Dark, self-disparaging tapes that play over and over in your mind can be countered:
  - Forgiveness is one key to freedom.
  - Gratitude goes a long way.
  - Be patient.
  - Expect progress to be slow and fraught with setbacks.
  - Recognize ANTS, objectively accept them, and dispose of them.
  - Employ Scripture, mottos, or mantras.
  - Relive happy moments from the past—savor the sights, sounds, smells, tastes, and emotions associated with them.
  - Surround yourself with mementos of joy: for example, photos; and those of success, such as awards and certificates.
- Over time, small rays of sunshine will break through the dark clouds in your mind.

- Incorporate daily routines to "train" your mind:
  - The daily discipline will help overcome inertia.
  - The daily discipline will also help bolster confidence.
- Nothing succeeds like success—daily practice of even a few of these disciplines will:
  - Help reframe the negative mindset of depression.
  - Provide a sense of control.
  - Give hope that things can get better.
  - Fortify a battered self-image and self-confidence.

CHAPTER 4

Sleep Is Not Optional

Refreshing sleep, along with regular exercise and a nutritious diet are the three pillars essential to good health. There is an extensive body of evidence promoting the benefits of adequate sleep. Conversely, the impact of inadequate sleep is profound. I have been a longtime proponent of sufficient sleep, but as my depression worsened, the ravages of chronic sleep deprivation took its toll on many fronts. Oh, how I longed for sleep! I craved refreshing, renewing, and restorative sleep. Two-and-a-half months into the course of my recovery, I made sure I took my antidepressant each day, saw my therapist, Dr. Perry, each week, and completed the "homework" he assigned. I noted that my body was more relaxed. I felt less jittery and on edge. My normal aches and pains were less severe. My energy level improved. Going to the gym was once again a joy and something I looked forward to, instead of a chore to be done because I knew it was "good for me."

My mentation also slowly improved. My negative ruminations diminished, and my focus and memory improved. I could more easily recall names of others, medications, and medical syndromes. I also could better remember what I read and studied, and more correctly recall conversations. This was a great relief—to know I was not suffering from premature dementia.

Sleep, however, remained elusive. I continued to have trouble both falling asleep and remaining asleep. I was now getting four or, on a good night, five hours of fitful sleep instead of the two or three hours of fitful sleep I had previously. Despite this improvement, I lamented, "If I could just get more sleep, I'd recover faster."

In the months leading up to my depression, I had worked diligently to improve my sleep. I employed sleep hygiene recommendations:

1. No TV in the bedroom.
2. Do not read in bed.
3. Only use the bedroom for sleep and sex.
4. Maintain a comfortable temperature in the bedroom.
5. Make the room as quiet and dark as possible (I tried white noise, such as waves, but this did not help me. I started wearing nightshades during my deployment to Iraq in 2010–2011 and I still use them.)
6. Establish a routine to wind down as bedtime approaches.
7. Drink some herbal tea or warm milk.
8. Avoid caffeine for at least six hours, and preferably eight, before bedtime.
9. Use melatonin from time to time.
10. Exercise daily.

By nature, I am a night owl. Yet, my profession as a doctor and my military service demanded I get up early, except on non-duty days. Over the years, if I was not sleepy as bedtime approached, I stayed up late to read, study, or, watch a late game on TV. Even on the nights when I turned the TV off at a reasonable hour, sleep could be elusive.

The year prior to my diagnosis of depression, I employed progressive relaxation, imagery, deep breathing, prayers centered on gratitude, and maintaining a gratitude journal before bedtime. If I went to bed and could not fall asleep after fifteen to twenty minutes, I got up and did something like reading or writing, until I felt sleepy, and then went back to bed. Many nights, in the nine to ten months leading up to my diagnosis, I repeated this routine three, four, and even eight times.

One of the cardinal rules of sleep hygiene is to go to bed and get up at the same time each day. Over the years, I found this the most difficult guideline to employ. On weekends and holidays when I did not have to work, I slept in. I also found myself staying up even later, on weekends and holidays. Non-adherence to a strict sleep schedule compounded my disrupted sleep.

Lack of sleep negatively impacts mood, mentation, and physical well-being. Reaction time is decreased, as is focus, concentration, and memory. Moreover, it increases inflammation, diminishes immunity, and lowers one's threshold for pain. When sleep-deprived, we become more irritable and impatient. Motivation wanes. We are less likely to exercise and we have less willpower to eat a healthy diet.

Part of this is due to hormonal changes with sleep deprivation. Lack of adequate sleep results in higher levels of ghrelin, a hormone that stimulates hunger. This prompts us to eat fatty foods and those with simple carbohydrates such as ice cream, donuts, and chocolate. Moreover, sleep deprivation decreases levels of leptin, a hormone that signals satiety. This negative double whammy, increased ghrelin and decreased leptin, contributes to poor eating habits and, in turn, to weight gain.

Did you ever pull an "all-nighter" to complete a work or school project? What was the common fare to eat? Probably something like pizza, soda, candy, cookies, hamburgers and fries? Of course, what self-respecting college student didn't enjoy the wonderful smell and even better taste of freshly popped popcorn? To top it off, popcorn had to be consumed with other delights, like soda.

To keep us going during "all-nighters" we drank lots of caffeinated beverages—coffee, tea, and soda. The following day we consumed caffeine throughout the day to help stave off, at least in part, fatigue and sleepiness. These heavy doses of caffeine made it hard to fall asleep when we finally went to bed.

Moreover, when we are under stress, adrenaline and the stress hormone cortisol flood our bloodstream and our sympathetic nervous system is on high alert. We are primed for battle, or at least a competitive athletic contest, but perform sub-optimally due to our sleep-deprived state. Being on high alert without having to flee or fight is damaging to our health and well-being. World-class athletes are keenly aware of the deleterious effects of sleep deprivation. They understand that adequate amounts of restful sleep are essential to improve their performance and allow them to recover more quickly and fully from arduous training. The Army has started to envision and treat its Soldiers as highly trained and valuable world-class athletes. Similarly, pilots recognize the importance of good sleep to remain alert, focused, and able to make wise decisions, during an unexpected contingency or crisis.

Throughout General Horoho's tenure as the U.S. Army Surgeon General promoting the benefits of restful sleep and sounding warnings of the negative impact of insufficient sleep, it was recognized how much sleep-deprivation in the U.S. Military impairs performance. This led to changes in battle operations, especially during continuous operations over extended periods. These continuous operations fostered requirements to employ work-rest cycles and promote improved sleep hygiene on the battlefield. It also highlighted the tragic deaths of Soldiers related to sleep deprivation while driving. Sleep deprivation is dangerous—it can kill you!

Conversely, if we get an adequate amount of refreshing sleep, we function better. Our mood improves. We have less pain and inflammation. Our immune system gets stronger. We recall information better, process information more quickly and accurately, and remember it better. Learning is improved by consolidating memories, along with enhancing focus and concentration. This leads to better decision-making, better use of resources, and more resilience to stress. Increased amounts of growth hormone are secreted, which is essential to cellular growth and repair. The brain is also bathed in cerebrospinal fluid which removes toxins and cellular debris. This list, although incomplete, shows how profoundly our sleep impacts our health and well-being. For many of us, stress profoundly impacts our sleep. Some may be prone to sleeping more when under significant stress. Unfortunately, I am in the camp that is plagued by insomnia or fitful sleep when I contend with severe stress.

Sleep, as with most aspects of our lives, is impacted by many things. It can relate to what and when we eat and drink; the type, intensity, duration, and time of day we exercise or the lack of exercise; family and work commitments; raising children or caring for aging parents; attendance at school or additional training; the shift we work and whether or not it changes; health issues (an enlarged prostate may cause you to get up repeatedly at night to urinate), obstructive sleep apnea, restless leg syndrome, chronic pain; a noisy or unsafe environment; exposure to sunlight and artificial light; medications; substances including tobacco, alcohol, and illicit drugs; and many others.

Behavioral health issues such as depression, anxiety, bipolar disorder, and PTSD also can all disrupt sleep. Poor sleep is often a hallmark of these disorders. In depression, it may be difficult to fall asleep. A person suffering from depression may also experience early morning awakenings (waking up in the wee hours or early morning well before your normal time to arise and being unable to fall back asleep). Although the reason for this phenomenon is not fully known, it is may be related to disruptions in one's circadian rhythm, in part, due to disruptions in the production/depletion of serotonin, melatonin, and other hormones essential for sound sleep. I, unfortunately, suffered from both the inability to fall asleep and to stay asleep. I employed most of the sleep hygiene techniques mentioned above and attempted to keep a consistent bedtime and time to arise. I tried to meditate to quiet my mind, but found it difficult to focus. Sleep remained elusive and I was certain my chronic sleep deprivation impeded my recovery.

I regularly discussed my concerns about my impaired sleep with my psychologist, Dr. Perry, my psychiatrist, and my primary care physician. We decided to add a medication to help improve my sleep. The first few nights after starting the medication were blissful. I awakened refreshed and with an overall improved sense of well-being. I began to note further improvements in my focus, concentration, memory, mood, and energy level. Facing my daily responsibilities became less arduous and my interest in activities such as coaching and watching wrestling, attending social functions, and interacting with others increased.

The improvements in my body, mentation, and mood, were all enhanced by the improvements in my sleep. I could sense my *joie de vivre* returning. It was not dramatic, but slowly and almost imperceptibly, the darkness, despair, and discouragement gave way to light, joy, and encouragement. My optimism was further buoyed.

Three to four months into my recovery, if I did not enjoy seven to eight hours of sound sleep, I readily felt the repercussions: I noted the decline in my overall sense of well-being. I was more irritable, jittery and impatient, and I had less motivation to eat a healthy diet and engage in my normal exercise routine. I found it harder to pray, meditate, read, and study. In fact, my psychiatrist repeatedly told me, "As your sleep goes, so goes your mood disorder." He readily recognized the importance of sufficient, sound sleep to my health and further instilled the importance of monitoring my sleep and adhering to good sleep hygiene. My wife, Sherry, is keenly aware of the paramount importance of sleep to my well-being and helps to arrange our lifestyle to accommodate and enhance my sleep. Thank you, my love.

While I trained for the U.S. Veterans National Freestyle Tournament, I was extra vigilant about sleep hygiene. I was dedicated to strict bedtimes. I trained vigorously and needed adequate refreshing sleep for my body to recover. This meant saying no to certain engagements that ran late or excusing myself early, to maintain my sleeping schedule. I also made myself turn off the TV earlier to avoid staying up too late to watch favorite teams play. Sleep became my friend and I treated it with renewed interest and care.

Lessons Learned

- Sleep is not optional.
    - It is essential to top performance.
    - It must be a priority, not an afterthought. Say "No!" to other activities, to say "Yes!" to sleep.
    - Plan ahead so you can stick to your sleep schedule.
        - Forewarn the host you will be leaving early, if the event is scheduled to run late.
        - When traveling, stick to your routine.

    - Plan ahead for weekends and holidays so you can stick to your routine.
    - Adherence to sleep hygiene makes you more productive.
    - Improved focus, concentration, and energy pay dividends beyond improved health and athletic performance.
  - "Just say, no!" to a TV in your bedroom:
    - Make this non-negotiable.
    - Turn off the TV early, preferably one hour before bed.
- You may want to experiment with your bedroom environment:
  - Install blackout curtains or wear nightshades.
  - Spray lavender on your sheets and pillows.
  - Use some white noise, such as a ticking clock or the sound of waves.
  - Turn down the temperature a few degrees at night; a cool room enhances sleep.
  - Invest in high quality silk sheets. This is one of my favorites, and I notice the difference when I travel (remember, self-care is not selfish).
  - Share a massage with your partner:
    - It can help relax you, and it induces the secretion of oxytocin, the love/bonding hormone.
    - Come to think of it, so does a long passionate goodnight kiss (hmmm).
  - Log your sleep

   - I track the quality and duration of my sleep with help of a Fitbit.
   - The Fitbit App synched to my phone allows me to track the duration and quality of my sleep on a daily and weekly basis.
   - Studies show that most of us are very inaccurate in judging the duration of our sleep without some objective measure.
- A sleep log is another way to track the quality of your sleep, based on how refreshed you feel when you awaken, on a 1–10-point scale.
- If you are like me, beware of reverting to old habits, such as:
   - Staying up too late.
   - Sleeping in on weekends and holidays.
   - Not adhering to a normal routine to wind down.
   - Drinking caffeine later in the day.
- Adherence to good sleep hygiene requires daily vigilance to reap the benefits of sleep.
- A brief time of prayer or meditation, before bedtime can help calm mind, body, and soul.
- Avoid projects you want to complete, once started, if they take you past your scheduled bedtime (I am all too familiar with this sleep disrupter).
- Naps that are 20–30 minutes long can refresh and clear your mind, rejuvenate your body, and improve your learning and memory.

- If you can nap without impacting your sleep at night, enjoy your *siestas*. Caution: If you find that napping interferes with your sleep at night, consider progressively shortening your nap time until you find the optimal duration. If you determine that even a short nap impairs your sleep at night, say *adios* to your nap, no matter how luxurious you find it. You can find other ways to pamper yourself.
- Sex? You may be thinking, "Dr. Mondragón said to only use the bedroom for sleep and sex. So, when is he going to talk about sex?"
    - Plan!
        - This may go against the grain for those of you who feel that sex should be a spontaneous event.
        - Remember, men, we are like frying pans and women like slow cookers.
    - If you are the parents of younger children or teens, you understand the importance of planning for an amorous evening.
    - Similarly, you and your partner may have demanding jobs and social responsibilities, so you want to be at your best.
    - Allow sex to be a highlight, not a frustrating and rushed afterthought.
    - Men, set time aside (before you or your partner are exhausted):

- This is an important, if not essential, part of your relationship, so don't leave it to chance.
- Your thoughtfulness will be well rewarded by your partner and you will look like a prince.
- An added benefit: the surge of serotonin, oxytocin, and other hormones associated with lovemaking and orgasm help elevate mood and induce sleep.

CHAPTER 5

Nutrition Nurtures Recovery

A nutritious diet, in addition to adequate sleep, is another key to recovery from depression. In the next chapter, I'll cover the "Big E"—Exercise—but in this chapter we'll talk about eating a nutritious diet.

I have a sweet tooth. I am especially fond of chocolate candy and ice cream. I really like popcorn and if I go to a movie I can down a *big* tub of buttered popcorn. I am, however, five-foot-five inches tall, over sixty years old, a Hispanic, and diabetes runs in my family. Not to mention, I tend to gain weight around my midsection. This is referred to being an apple, as opposed to a pear. (I will discuss the significance of this later.) I list the above to indicate that I have many risk factors for developing Diabetes Mellitus. I do not want to develop diabetes, or to increase my risk of other diseases due to poor eating and being overweight. Consequently, a nutritious diet is paramount for my physical well-being and functioning, as well as for mental performance.

In amateur wrestling, you compete in a specified weight class. Wrestlers must learn to manage their eating habits and their weight for optimal performance. I competed at the 112-pound class in high school, 118 pounds in college, 123–125.5 pounds after college, and 127.6 pounds (58 kilograms) as a veteran (old-timer). I have practiced both healthy and unhealthy ways to manage my weight. Now, I am dedicated to healthy eating.

First let me dispense with the unhealthy ways "to cut weight for wrestling." These include:

1. "Starving" yourself; eating very little three to four days before a match. This, as you might imagine, makes you feel miserable.
2. Restricting your fluid intake. This makes you feel even more miserable.
3. Working out intensely, dressed in sweats.
4. Enduring numbers one, two, and three, and then the *coup de grâce*: sitting in a sauna to shed the last pound, or in some cases, last half-pound, to make competition weight.

These tactics, practiced by some wrestlers are not only unhealthy, but can be dangerous. I am sorry to say that I followed some of these practices during parts of my high school and college wrestling days. I am not proud of this fact.

Severely restricting calories when competing in wrestling slowed my metabolism. This made it even harder to manage my weight. In addition to this, I was breaking down my muscles to provide fuel for my body. Losing muscle mass is not what a wrestler wants to do. When I "starved" myself to make weight, I did not understand how it damaged my body and impeded my optimal performance.

Nutrition is not only about what you eat, but how you eat, and how you develop a relationship with food and eating habits. For example, if you follow one of the many diet fads to quickly shed pounds, it can be detrimental to your overall well-being and results in a slowed metabolism, which can result in loss of muscle tissue. This practice often yields the very outcome you don't want—rapid weight gain when you return to your old eating habits, which is complicated by a slower metabolism and a gain of fat at the expense of muscle mass. This can lead to the "yo-yo effect" of repeated episodes of rapid weight loss, followed by rapid weight gain, often ultimately exceeding your starting weight, and with added physical consequences.

To be successful, healthy nutrition, along with healthy exercise and sleep habits must become part of your lifestyle. Plan to incorporate them into your day-to-day life. I like to eat. I come from a family of great cooks. My wife is a fabulous cook. I told you about some of the snacks I enjoy. Eating a nutritious diet—or you may wish to call it a healthy eating plan—requires planning, preparation, and persistence. It helps to have accountability partners. It can be done. You owe it to yourself.

I mentioned my poor eating habits at other times in my life, now let me speak to the healthy changes I made. Drawing from the dietary regimen I incorporated when I trained for the 2012 and 2013 U.S. National Veterans Freestyle Wrestling

Championships, these are the healthy changes I made. I chose to:

1. Always eat breakfast.
2. Start the day off with a breakfast that included a generous portion of high-quality protein and healthy fat. A favorite of mine is one to two whole eggs scrambled with egg whites, cut vegetables ("veggies" such as peppers, spinach, tomatoes), topped with salsa and a healthy fat, like avocado.
3. Eat every three to four hours.
4. Increase the intake of leafy green vegetables (although I already ate generous portions of these).
5. Incorporate healthy snacks, such as almonds, cheese sticks, sliced veggies or fruit.
6. Restrict my carbohydrate intake at supper and avoid simple carbohydrate snacks, especially at night.
7. Drink more water. A bottle with a carbon filter became my constant companion in my car, at work, and in the gym or wrestling room.
8. Keep healthy snacks on hand and place items such as sliced vegetables or fruit at eye level in the refrigerator.
9. Ask my wife not to buy items such as ice cream, candy, or chips when grocery shopping.
10. Preparing for dining out or social events. Sometimes I ate a healthy snack before we left the house, to quell my hunger.

My strategy was never to allow myself to become ravenous. My activity level increased, preparing to compete: I exercised twice a day, six days a week. I could see my body composition slowly change over a period of months, while shedding fat to trim down from 136 to 127.6 pounds, and increasing muscle mass. It worked. I easily made weight and went on to win the National Championship in 2012, and Runner-Up in 2013. These changes in my day-to-day eating habits have served me well since then.

I've even come to understand that many of my diet changes are also brain-healthy. A diet rich in a variety of fresh vegetables, fruits, fish, seeds, and nuts, such as the Mediterranean Diet, both decreases inflammation and the risk of depression. Foods rich in omega-3 fatty acids such as salmon, halibut, almonds, seeds such as pumpkin, chia, hemp, and flax, along with avocados, provide precursors to the brain to make serotonin. Serotonin is depleted in depression and many of the primary anti-depressants used today are aimed at increasing the level of serotonin in the brain. The medical community is also learning that many of our common diseases are linked to inflammation—heart disease, diabetes, various types of arthritis, pain syndromes, etc.

A diet rich in sugar, saturated fat, and processed foods promotes inflammation. Moreover, being fat, especially intra-abdominal fat, promotes inflammation. Fat is not inert. It secretes chemicals that incite inflammation. Research has shown that the gastrointestinal tract does far more than break down, absorb, and transport nutrients, and then remove waste. Our guts are an incredible mass of neural tissue, the enteric nervous system, and a finely balanced microbiome made up of bacteria that number ten times the number of cells in our body.

The enteric nervous system is composed of more neurons than found in either the spinal cord or the peripheral nervous system, and produces a variety of neurotransmitters, including the majority of serotonin found in the body. Our gut microbiome is a balance of good and bad bacteria. A healthy diet keeps the bad bacteria in check. Processed foods and food additives and preservatives, along with sugars, damage and disrupt the gut microbiome and this results in less serotonin production. Serotonin is important to optimizing our mood and tranquility. It is also a precursor of melatonin, which is important to our sleep. Yes, indulging in highly processed food is bad for our bodies, and for our brains! Truly, we are what we eat.

Fat is the enemy of wrestlers. We don't like it! We fight against it day in and day out. We understand the perils of fat. We look at ourselves the mirror and we weigh ourselves, in the morning, before and after practice, and before bedtime. Some of these same practices can benefit you in your fight against fat. Look at yourself in a full-length mirror when naked. What do you see? When I look in the mirror, I am looking for indications of "love handles." Are your clothes fitting tighter? I notice tighter fitting pants and shirts when I gain as little as 4–6 pounds of fat.

There are additional ways to track your body composition. One is measuring your BMI (body mass index), calculated as weight in kilograms divided by height in centimeters. A healthy BMI is 20-25. This measure is frequently used by healthcare professionals. For the average person, it is a reasonable measure. It is a poor measure for the lean and very muscular individual or the one that is skinny on the outside and fat on the inside (SOFI). An individual who is a SOFI is skinny because they lack muscle mass, but are fat because of the visceral fat around their internal organs. They may not look bad, but they are not healthy. Your waist size is another way to track body composition. A general rule of thumb is a waist measurement of greater than 35 inches for women or 40 inches for men increases the risk of diabetes and a host of other diseases. Note, for those of us who are smaller, along with Filipinos, and Asians these measurements are "overly generous" and don't serve as a reliable gauge.

Another way to track body composition is to use a scale that incorporates an impedance meter to calculate body fat. Although this method may not be the most accurate, it will help you monitor trends. If used with your body weight, visual appearance, and waist circumference, you can readily monitor your body composition. A before-and-after photo is a dramatic way to track your progress. Photographs taken at different intervals in your life can help provide visual reference and motivation to maintain your healthy eating plan.

Posting an old photo of yourself at a healthier weight/body composition on your refrigerator can also serve as motivation to maintain improved nutritional habits. You may choose to place this old photo next to your current "before" photo as a prominent reminder of your goal. When I was flabby and out of shape, looking at old photos of when I was in tip-top shape served as additional motivation to adhere to a healthy diet, engage in regular exercise, and give attention to sleep.

Remember I mentioned there is a significance to having an "apple-shape" body or a "pear shape?" If your body shape is "apple," like mine is, you tend to gain your weight around your waist. A "pear-shape" body preferentially gains weight in the hips and buttocks. Although we may lament looking like either of these, it is less healthy if you are an apple. This is because truncal fat generally reflects intra-abdominal fat. Remember intra-abdominal fat is not neutral. Fat is metabolically active! It promotes inflammation.

Intra-abdominal fat is not the fat you can pinch between two fingers, but it is the fat surrounding organs in the body. Intra-abdominal fat secretes hormones and inflammatory mediators that negatively impact the body. For example, this fat predisposes you to insulin resistance. Insulin resistance, in turn, is a precursor of Type 2 Diabetes Mellitus (non-insulin dependent diabetes). Insulin resistance often accompanies obesity, hypertension (high blood pressure), and hypercholesterolemia (high cholesterol). It also increases the risk of heart disease and cancers such as colon cancer. In short, excess intra-abdominal fat is unhealthy.

Regular exercise, adequate sleep, and wholesome nutrition go hand-in-hand. My brother Chris, a personal trainer, tells his clients, "You cannot out-train a bad diet!" I understand this very well. Don't become a casualty of unhealthy eating and poor nutritional habits.

One of the dietary no-no's Americans are especially prone to is excessive portion sizes. Several years ago, I helped teach CPR and Advanced Cardiac Life Support to members of the State Department at a course held in Lisbon, Portugal. A colleague and I ate out at a different restaurant each night. Meals took a few hours to eat, and the portion sizes were very reasonable. I finished a meal without feeling stuffed. When I returned to the United States, the first time I went out to eat I noted the stark difference in portion size compared to the portions served in Portugal.

Prior to my trip to Portugal, I had become accustomed to super-sized portions. My growing waist and increasing weight showed it. I had to rein in my portion size in order to fit comfortably into pants and uniforms. Besides, I didn't want to feel self-conscious, and even embarrassed, when I took my shirt off or wore swimming trunks. No self-respecting lightweight wrestler wants a big flabby gut! At my age, I still feel this way. Yes, pride is at work, but more importantly, I understand the negative impact this fat has on my health and well-being.

Maintaining a healthy weight and waist size requires a daily commitment. When one is in the grip of depression, the idea of eating a healthy diet may be overwhelming. Pick one thing that you can do and stick with it for a week. For example, resolve to eat a healthy breakfast each morning. It may require planning ahead with shopping, and prep time, such as cutting up vegetables the day before. As with any successful endeavor, we build in habits and routines to make to make our lives simpler, easier, and some tasks "no brainers." If that is too much, resolve to eat healthy snacks such as small apples and small packs of nuts, and keep these on hand. Look to make it easier for you to succeed. If you have a partner, friend, church member who can assist, their support and encouragement can go a long way. After a week, add another simple step to improve your nutrition. If you gradually add healthy habits into your routine, eventually, and cumulatively, they will add up to a healthier lifestyle.

Health-enhancing nutrition, just like regular exercise and adequate sleep, must be incorporated into your daily routine. There are no quick fixes. Those ubiquitous television programs that advocate rapid and dramatic weight loss portray selected participants determined to lose weight. Participants are assigned personal trainers who help them to progressively adjust their workouts so that they gradually challenge their bodies and stimulate their metabolism. Likewise, they make significant adjustments to their diets, strictly limit access to highly-processed and junk food, have ready access to healthy foods, and on-site instruction in meal preparation. They also sequester participants away from family, friends, and fun. Participants are pitted against each other to achieve the greatest percentage of weight loss. They are freed from the normal distractions and duties of day-to-day life. For many participants, their weight loss is not sustainable when they return home because they fail to change their lifestyle. A change in lifestyle is required. There are no quick fixes.

Healthy living is just that, a lifestyle. If it is not sustainable, it will fail. Most of us have many competing demands for our time, attention, and energy. Family, work, social commitments, financial constraints, and health issues, to name a few. Incorporating healthy lifestyle changes must be a priority; they cannot be left to chance. Preparation, planning, and persistence all come into play.

Preparation for nutritious eating includes learning new nutrition-packed, tasty recipes, shopping with a list, and making healthy snacks an easier choice. Planning menus before shopping and devising strategies in advance when going out to eat or attending a function where food is served are important. For most of us, we must remove foods laden with sugar and our favorite highly-processed snacks from our shopping carts or from our homes. In my case this includes ice cream, chocolate candy, and chips. Persist. Make a choice each day to eat a *healthy* diet. If you fail, do not let this unravel your commitment to an improved lifestyle. Instead, resume your enhanced food plan with your next meal. Remember your commitment to a healthier lifestyle, not a quick fix. It must be sustainable.

As a wrestler, I would succumb to a bowl of ice cream from time to time. Then I'd reason, "Oh, well, since I've already broken my diet, I might as well eat some cookies, too." This kind of mentality can derail you. You must prepare for such situations. We are not robots and we will get off track, especially when it comes to changing our lifestyles regarding exercise, sleep, and diet. Accept you've derailed, don't beat yourself up, and choose to resume your healthy alternatives. It can be done. You can do it. It may require the help of an accountability partner. Your significant other, a family member, or a friend or co-worker can be enlisted to help you remain accountable. These accountability partners must be committed to your success, and not seek to derail you.

"Let's go to McDonald's." "We're calling out for pizza; what would you like?" "You have got to try some of this birthday cake. Let me get you a slice." If your so-called accountability partners are saying this to you, dump them and find others who have your best interest in mind. Beware: sometimes it is family and friends who will unwittingly seek to derail you. You must prepare for these situations, have a plan to firmly and graciously say no, and not feel guilty for doing so.

Now, let me share something very important from the perspective of a doctor. Many patients lament, "Doc, I'm doomed. Everyone in my family is fat. I've always been fat. It's my genes!" I have heard it said, "We are our genes, but our genes are not our destiny." We can shape how our genes respond and which of our genes we turn on or off. Epigenetics is the study of how this phenomenon takes places. Science is learning how our genetic makeup, our genome, is expressed. Various factors affect gene expression, which is turning certain genes on and others off. Some of these factors include: our environment, diet, exercise, sleep, relationships, optimism, stress management, level of contentment, etc. Remember, we cannot alter our genome, but we can dramatically shape the expression of our genes to improve our health and well-being.

Lessons Learned

- Never skip breakfast.
- Ensure you incorporate adequate high-quality protein with each meal.

- Fish, eggs, egg whites, lentils, beans, almonds, and walnuts are healthy options.
- Drink more water. Sometimes we may sense we are hungry, when in fact we are thirsty.
- Do not skip meals.
- Do not go longer than three to four hours without eating.
- Eat smaller portions.
- Eat on smaller plates and/or eat from red plates: these two techniques make your brain sense you've eaten more than you have, and help you feel satiated more quickly.
- S-l-o-w down when eating.
    - If you cannot eat your entire meal slowly, savor the first three bites of every food you eat.
    - Enjoy the sight, smell, texture, and unique flavor of each food.
    - Put your fork or spoon down after each bite.
- Do not eat while watching TV. (Remember the big tub of buttered popcorn I devoured at the movies?)
- If you eat when distracted, you will eat far more than you intended to.
- Enlist accountability partners.
- Don't buy junk food—get rid of the junk in your pantry or refrigerator.
- Plan menus before shopping. (Beware: Don't go grocery shopping if you are hungry. This will make you more prone to buy junk food).

- Incorporate healthy snacks. Keep sliced veggies and fruit readily available—in front, at eye-level in your refrigerator.
- Eat more fresh fruits and vegetables—the more colorful the better; think of a rainbow of colors.
- Just say NO to sugary drinks.
- Don't let dining out derail you.
- Eat a salad or sliced veggies before you eat anything else.
    - Ask for veggies in lieu of bread or ask that bread not be served.
    - Eat a consommé before the main course.
    - Cut your main course in two and ask your waiter to put half of it in a container, before you start.
- If attending a function where food will be served, have a healthy snack before leaving home.
    - If possible, upon arrival load up on veggies and select a healthy protein.
    - Bypass the dessert tables: eat some fruit instead.
- Limit alcohol intake. (One weight loss doctor I knew said drinking alcohol was "like drinking fat.")
- Our diet is essential in the production of serotonin.
- Our gut is host to our biome which produces most of our serotonin.
- Highly processed foods and sugar are detrimental to our biome.

- A diet rich in fresh vegetables, fruits, nuts, seeds, and fatty fish is beneficial and promotes serotonin production.
- We cannot change our genes, but we can turn our genes on and off by our lifestyle; our genes do not dictate our destiny!

CHAPTER 6

Exercise Combats Depression

I had just won my first wrestling match. Wow, the exhilaration was intoxicating! Two years of training, and now, June 1970, I enjoyed the spoils of victory. Over the course of that day I wrestled five matches to win the tournament. Countless hours spent training, both on the wrestling mats and off, rope skipping, performing push-ups, sit-ups, pull-ups, along with running. My body was up to the task. I tasted victory and this spurred me on to even more intense training.

About the same time, I discovered wrestling, I read Dr. Kenneth Cooper's book, *Aerobics.* I was intrigued by his clear explanation of how physical activity such as running, swimming, or biking tax the cardiovascular system, requiring more oxygen. Dr. Cooper explained the benefits of improved cardiovascular fitness and health by exercising regularly at a moderate pace for an adequate duration. This book increased my love affair with exercise. I have been an advocate of exercise since then.

I am the product of regularly taxing my body and I enjoy many of its benefits. In fact, in some circles you would call me a gym rat. The ambience—the sights, sounds, smells, and excitement of wrestling rooms, workout rooms, and gyms—have been part of my fabric for over fifty years. I've learned many strategies to start and sustain an exercise program, the appropriate "dose" required, and I have probably heard almost every excuse you can imagine from my patients about why they "can't exercise."

Alas, I have not always exercised wisely. At times I exercised too little, such as when I was in medical school and residency. At other times I over-exercised, failed to listen to my body, and suffered overuse injuries.

One does not necessarily need to exercise intensely to benefit. In fact, unless you have a high level of overall fitness, I recommend you *not* engage in intense exercise. If you are over forty and are sedentary, and especially if you suffer from diseases such as diabetes, high blood pressure, COPD, and most certainly cardiovascular disease, please see your doctor before you embark on an exercise program. Think of proper dosing as duration, frequency, and intensity. The general recommendation by medical groups, such as the American Heart Association, American Diabetic Association, and Centers for Disease Control, is to perform thirty minutes of moderate intensity aerobic activity five or more days a week.

"Moderate" is relative to your level of fitness, and would be a brisk walk for most, a jog for some, and a run for others. You should be able to carry on a conversation when you are exercising if you're in the "moderate" zone. Note, you can gain benefit from aerobic activity (walking, running, biking, swimming, hiking, rowing, dancing skiing, etc.), even if this exercise is broken up into two or three, 10–15-minute segments, respectively. If you are new to an exercise program it is far better to begin slow and make steady progress than to start off "guns blazing" and become very sore, or worse, injure yourself and then lose interest. Instead, consider your exercise program as an investment in your health that will provide dividends the rest of your life. Try it; you'll like it.

Exercise should be proceeded by a warm-up to loosen joints, ligaments and muscles, and to increase your heart rate—to limit the possibility of injury and to improve your performance. Most often you see individuals warming up using static stretches (described as a passive warm-up). Save these for after a workout. Static stretches are exactly that—stretching and holding the stretch for several seconds. This type of stretch and warm-up decreases strength by approximately ten percent. Instead, engage in an active warm-up, one where you are moving. For example, if you are going to walk, you can spend a few minutes performing squats, toe raises, side bends, arm circles or swings, and walk slowly at the outset, before picking up your pace. If you wish to perform static stretches, with some more calisthenics such as squats, push-ups, sit-ups, etc. during your cool-down, great. Otherwise, you can slow your pace down the last four to five minutes of your workout for your cool-down. It is important to do a warm-up and cool-down to loosen your body and increase your heart rate before you exercise, and to allow your heart rate to decrease slowly at the end of exercise.

Wrestlers delight in eking out one more push-up, chin-up, or heavy barbell squat. As coaches we tell our wrestlers, "If two wrestlers are equally skilled, the advantage goes to the stronger wrestler." I have known some wrestlers who were incredible technicians, but because they refused to spend time in the weight room, they never stood on the championship podium.

Strength training is often overlooked and is one of the best markers of independent function as we age. The medical term for loss of muscle mass is sarcopenia. The key to preventing, and even reversing, sarcopenia is strength training coupled with a nutritious diet, and adequate amounts of regular refreshing sleep. Maintaining muscle mass is essential to help increase metabolism, especially as we age or have been sedentary, to help maintain a healthy weight and stave off belly fat. Strength training and aerobic exercise boost endorphins to elevate mood, and also improves sleep, memory, concentration, and cardiovascular health; lowers blood sugar, blood pressure, and cholesterol; helps decrease pain, stress, and weight; improves lean body mass (muscle and bones). In addition to this, it gives a shot of confidence and encouragement, which are in short supply when you're depressed.

It can be a struggle just to get out of bed, let alone think about exercising. The joy, satisfaction, and exertion of one's will to accomplish even a very short workout on a regular basis can help to overcome inertia that accompanies depression. It's more than depletion of emotional and physical energy; motivation, hope, and purpose are lacking. Success in achieving a regular workout can help promote success in other areas to enhance recovery from depression. Remember, nothing begets success like success. Make it easy for yourself. Set a small goal, 2–3 minutes to start with, and stick to it. Once you begin to achieve this goal and get moving, you will want to do more.

Some wrestlers come into the wrestling room and they are skinny, soft, and smooth. They lack muscle mass and it not only shows in their appearance, but their performance. They struggle to control, attack, or lift an opponent. They lack "horsepower." These wrestlers fall into the category of "SOFI"—skinny on the outside and fat on the inside—as previously discussed. This results in two negative consequences. Lack of muscle mass increases their risk of injury and contributes to an inferior performance, which, in turn, discourages them. I take these wrestlers aside, along with their parents, and encourage them to establish a strength training program. Those who take my advice become better wrestlers and enjoy more success.

What exercises are best? Previously I introduced the "BIG 3" of overall physical well-being: sleep, nutrition and exercise in general. Now I want to introduce the "BIG 3" exercises critical to muscular strength and function: squat, push, and pull. These three movements are the most important and engage the largest muscle groups of the body: hips/buttocks/legs, chest, and back, respectively. A squat is just that. A pushing movement can be a push-up starting on a counter and progressing to a chair, your knees on the floor and then hands and feet, or a bench press with a barbell or machine. A pulling motion can be a rowing motion using a barbell, dumbbell, machine, or the all-time great, the chin-up.

How much exercise? Start with ten repetitions (one set) of light weights (or body weight such as when doing push-ups), and do two sets, every other day. After two weeks, increase to three sets of ten repetitions. Then you can start to increase repetitions slowly to fifteen. After this, begin to increase the weight. This slow progression will allow your muscles, tendons, and ligaments time to adapt, so you will be less likely to suffer an overuse injury. Besides, when you're are in the throes of depression, your energy is often limited. After your first two to three months you can increase weight when you reach eight to ten repetitions. If you don't have access to weights or machines, fill up a pint, quart, half-gallon, and gallon-sized empty milk containers with sand. These will provide weight for squats and rowing and you can perform push-ups. If two sets are too much, start with one.

The excuse for not exercising I hear most often is, "I don't have time." My answer is always the same: break your aerobic exercise into short bouts of five to ten minutes before work, and before and after lunch. As well, you can park at the furthest corner of the parking lot, take the stairs instead of an elevator, etc. Perform your sets of strength training exercises without rest. This will give you the added benefit of an additional aerobic benefit by keeping your heart rate elevated.

Here are some other common excuses I have encountered, coupled with answers to counter them. Practice saying them to yourself until they become who you are rather than what you do:

Excuse: I don't know how.

Answer: Google these exercises and watch them on YouTube or go to the library and check out a book or two with illustrations (you don't even need to read them). Later, if you can afford it, join a gym, or hire a personal trainer.

Excuse: I just can't seem to get started.

Answer: Enlist the help of a friend or family member to exercise with you at a specific time each day. This accountability can go a long way.

Excuse: I don't like to exercise.

Answer: Combine your exercise with something you do enjoy, such as music, or chatting with a friend while you walk, or walking your dog. You might set up a stationary bike or treadmill in front of the TV and watch reruns of your favorite programs. Perhaps, more importantly, find an activity you enjoy and can sustain on a long-term basis, such as walking, biking, dancing, etc. The most important thing is to get moving.

Depression can sap you of your energy, motivation, and hope. So, you may feel and think, "Why bother?" Although overcoming this inertia may require significant effort, it will pay off in dividends. If nothing else, try to walk around for two minutes every hour and do some push-ups, squats, and some type of rows daily. Get moving! Exercise will not only benefit you in the short-term, but also in the long-term, helping to build resilience to weather the storms of life.

Lessons Learned

- Exercise improves:
  - Mood.
  - Sleep.
  - Concentration.
  - Memory.
  - Cardiovascular health and fitness.
  - Strength.
  - Blood pressure, blood sugar, and cholesterol.
  - Pain control.
  - Confidence and self-image.
  - Resilience.
- Exercise, healthy nutrition, and refreshing sleep are essential to recover from depression.
- "Start low and go slow"—start with a low dose of exercise and build up slowly to avoid injuries.
- Select activities you enjoy and can sustain.
- Enlist the help of a work-out/accountability buddy.
- Track your progress: if nothing else, document the days you perform aerobic and strength training.
- Incorporate the major muscle groups using the "BIG 3."
- Start with a warm-up and end with a cool-down.
- GET MOVING! Even if you can only do 3–5 minutes of exercise a day.

CHAPTER 7

Water-A Forgotten Elixir

"Hit the showers!" These were words we were so happy to hear at the end of high school wrestling practice. After a grueling sixty–ninety-minute practice, we ran wind sprints at the end of practice. These were timed sprints, and if you ran a sprint over the time limit, you were "rewarded" with an extra sprint. As the season wore on, required sprint times decreased and the number of sprints increased. Moreover, if our coaches felt we did not push ourselves in practice, we "enjoyed" extra sprints. Yes, we gleefully welcomed the wonderful sound of, "Hit the showers!"

It was glorious to stand under a blasting shower after an arduous practice. The massage-like effect of the water and the water's heat eased the ache and fatigue of our sore muscles. It also served as a time of transition to allow us to relax and prepare for the evening of studying that awaited after eating supper. Yes, this wonderful shower was therapeutic.

The therapeutic effect of water has been known for millennia. The ancient Greeks and Romans were renowned for their hot bathhouses. Today, many enjoy the relaxation associated with soaking in a hot tub after a long, difficult, and demanding day. Others derive immense pleasure lounging in a hot whirlpool. The sensation of dipping into a cool pool, lake, or river on a scorching summer day is wondrous. Children laugh, squeal, and dance with delight running through a fountain or sprinkler on blazing summer day. Truly, water is an elixir to both body and mind. Wrestlers are well acquainted with the healing properties of water. Ankle, knee, and finger or thumb sprains are common for wrestlers. We soak these body parts in ice baths, hot whirlpools, and sometimes alternating the ice bath or hot water to ease the swelling and pain, and promote healing.

Hydration is of supreme importance to the average person, and particularly to athletes; the practice of denying oneself free access to water during and after training is detrimental both physically and mentally. Even a small amount of dehydration, for example, 1–2 percent of total bodyweight, is detrimental to optimal performance for a wrestler. Thirsty wrestlers cannot perform at their optimal level. Olympians and other world-class athletes are very well-versed in the importance of good hydration and avoid dehydration as they train and compete.

In fact, even if you're not a wrestler, your brain and other organs do not work as efficiently if you are not well hydrated. Dehydration makes us more sluggish, and in certain circumstances, predisposes us to heat injuries. Water makes up the largest percentage of our body mass, 60–70 percent, and the brain is over 70 percent water. Why then do we reach for so many other drinks, when we can enjoy the refreshing and renewing properties of a cold glass of water?

Some of the reasons we don't drink enough water include:

- Water can seem boring and bland.
- Flavored drinks are readily available and very heavily marketed.
- We've grown accustomed to drinking flavored drinks—soda, an endless array of flavored and sweetened coffee, tea, and energy drinks.
- Sugar is addictive!
- We keep other drinks on hand throughout the day, instead of water!
- Tap water, depending on where you live, may not taste good.
- The way we have been raised. In some households, water was not promoted as the preferred drink. Instead a variety of juices and other flavored drinks were the typical fare, in lieu of water.
- We do not keep water at hand during work, exercise, and when we travel.
- We have not developed the habit of drinking water.
- We do not associate water with some of the foods we may eat. When was the last time you saw someone drinking water with their fried chicken, pizza, or hamburger and fries?
- We preferentially stock our refrigerators with a variety of other drinks instead of a pitcher of water placed where it is most readily available.

Systems and routines are essential to help us establish healthy habits. If you recall, earlier I gave recommendations to place fresh vegetables and fruits at eye level in the refrigerator, and to have nuts, fruits, or seeds readily available to snack on to control the urge to visit a drive-thru window or a vending machine. Routines help set us up for success and make healthier choices. For example, before I go to bed, I fill a large 16- ounce glass with water from our carbon filter water pitcher and set it next to the coffee maker. When I get up in the morning, I do not have to think about drinking my water; it's waiting for me. Likewise, I jumpstart my day with a short five- or six-minute workout that incorporates push, pull, squat, and a few core exercises. I do this workout not so much for the exercise, although there is some benefit, but more to wake me up before my devotions and for the sheer daily discipline it instills in me.

I've built these practices into my nighttime and morning routines to make it easier to drink my water, complete a short workout, and feel more awake and attentive for my morning devotions. When we're in the throes of depression and struggling with motivation, confidence, and energy, routines that empower us to succeed are even more important. Success begets success. Building healthy routines into our lives and imprinting them as habits, can provide a daily dose of encouragement. Moreover, it can preserve the precious supply of mental energy and resolve for other decisions.

Water is an elixir. My stepfather, Edward L. Luben—my "Daddyo"—enjoyed and touted Colorado's water. After a long drink of cool water, he'd say with a twinkle in his eye, "The man who created this certainly knew what he was doing!" I couldn't agree more. Water is essential to our health and well-being and, alas, undervalued.

The brain is sensitive to even mild dehydration. If you are dehydrated your thinking and overall function are impaired. You owe it to your brain to drink enough water. You may drink lots of unsweetened coffee or tea and think you're covered. Remember, I like coffee too! But caffeine, like alcohol, promotes diuresis, the loss of water, so it can predispose you to dehydration.

A few other scenarios are worth commenting on. Recall, we can mistake thirst for hunger. This is especially the case if you sense hunger an hour or two after a healthy and satisfying meal. We can also mistake thirst for fatigue, especially during that mid-afternoon slump that many of us experience at times. We think we're tired but instead we're dehydrated. A glass of water and we perk right up, just like a dehydrated potted houseplant. Another occasion we are prone to get dehydrated is when traveling. Airplane cabins have very low humidity and water loss occurs imperceptibly through the lungs and evaporation. This is referred to as insensible water loss.

Dry climates also promote insensible water loss. I grew up in Colorado and understand this well. Colorado's climate is semi-arid, so, insensible water loss is increased. I have learned when I travel and when I visit dry climates to make a more conscious effort to remain well hydrated.

Another common scenario for many of us is that we become busy, preoccupied, and distracted for hours at a time. I notice this particularly on clinic days, rushing from one patient to the next. A few hours may pass before I realize I have not had a drink of water. This does not promote optimal performance. Remember, water is an elixir.

11 Reminders to Drink Your Elixir

1. Start the day with at least 12–16 ounces of water, first thing in the morning. You are slightly dehydrated after a night's rest. On the day of a weigh-in, wrestlers have this down to a science. We call this "drift." We know we will lose 1–1 ½ pounds overnight due to insensible water loss.
2. I generally drink at least 16 ounces of water within minutes after I awaken. It may take time to adjust to drinking 12–16 ounces of water all at once, if you do not regularly drink water. It may require drinking it 4–6 ounces at a time.
3. Once you become accustomed to drinking water first thing in the morning, you will realize you feel and function better when you do so. Conversely, you will note a decrement in how you feel and function on the days you fail to hydrate first thing in the morning. Remember, the brain is over 70 percent water and the body 60 percent.
4. It is important to make adequate hydration a priority, just as it is to make healthy nutrition, adequate sleep, and regular exercise part of daily routines.
5. Keep water readily on hand. A favorite of mine is a water bottle with a carbon filter. It is close by when I

drive to work, sit at my desk, go to the gym, and travel. It is reusable, so I also make a small contribution to a healthier environment. It is very convenient when I attend sporting events or travel. I empty it and carry it through security and then fill it up at a water fountain.

6. Keep a pitcher of water at eye level and in front in the refrigerator. A pitcher with a carbon filter is very handy and can be refilled throughout the day.
7. If you tire of plain water, add some zest to a pitcher of water with mint, orange, lemon, or lime slices, or, even strawberries. Consider soda water for a change.
8. If you feel hungry, drink a glass of water first to ensure this sensation is not due to thirst, masking itself as hunger. Besides, drinking a glass of water before a meal may limit the amount of food eaten, because it helps to fill you up. As a result, you'll eat less food before the stomach signals the brain that it is full.
9. Remind yourself to drink water throughout the day. To establish this habit, it may be helpful to set a reminder in your phone, computer, or other mobile device.
10. Try to drink at a minimum, eight, 8-ounce glasses of water daily. Remember, if you travel, exercise, or are in a dry climate this amount may be woefully inadequate.
11. Enjoy the calming, restorative, and enjoyable powers of water, whether it is a hot shower, bath, or whirlpool, a dip in a cool pool, or to play with kids in a fountain. Water is a magical balm to both your body and soul.

"The man who created this sure knew what he was doing!" – Edward L. Luben

Lessons Learned

- Water is the elixir of life.
- Drink at least eight, 8-ounce glasses of water each day.
- Drink water first thing in the morning.
- Keep a water bottle handy (consider a refillable bottle with a replaceable carbon filter).
- The brain is sensitive to even mild dehydration If you are dehydrated your thinking and overall function are impaired.
- If you are depressed, dehydration only worsens how you are feeling and thinking.
- Stay attentive to hydration if you are exercising or performing manual labor.
- Beware of insensible (imperceptible) water loss when you sleep, travel, or are in a hot, dry climate.
- If you tire of the lack of taste of plain water, "jazz" it up.
- Thirst can masquerade as hunger or fatigue.

Water refreshes, soothes, and heals us in its many forms. Enjoy and appreciate this life-giving liquid. Drink up. *Salud!*

CHAPTER 8

Prevention Always Trumps Rehab

"Oh, that feels good!" I was on a table in the Physical Therapy Clinic with a large wrap on my left thigh through which ice water circulated. It was my reward after a demanding session to rehabilitate a severe hamstring strain. Eight months earlier, a month after I won the 58-kilogram Veterans National Championship, I suffered a partial tear of my left hamstring during a workout with high school wrestlers. It took almost three months of physical therapy to fully recover from my initial injury. Now I was back in therapy—ugh!

The first injury occurred during a normal workout. The second, however, was self-inflicted. My pride, foolishness, and competitiveness, were to blame. I suffered an over-use injury. A new colleague of mine, an accomplished judo player, started a judo class and invited me to practice. I was determined to make a good showing. After all, I'm a wrestler! Practice consisted of a prescribed and demanding warm-up, followed by several moves to learn basics—rolls, how to break a fall, footwork for throws, and foot sweeps. We practiced these moves without a partner.

Being a newcomer, my colleague and coach wanted me to learn some fundamentals before I sparred. In part, to avoid injury and to learn the basics in preparation to learn throws and submission holds. In my third week of practice, I arrived late to practice due to work commitments. I jumped right into my warm-up. I then practiced multiple repetitions of moves. Coach was busy demonstrating and observing the experienced judo players, in preparation for a competition. He assigned me to practice a foot sweep. So, I commenced to practice, practice, and practice.

After ten minutes, I began to note a twinge of pain in my hamstrings. I ignored it. I did not want to complain and look like a wimp. I continued to practice this move for a long time. Eventually Coach came and showed me some judo grappling techniques. We concluded with some light sparring. Afterwards my hamstrings were sore. After a cool-down and shower, my hamstrings were tight and increasingly sore. The damage was done! By the next day, I could not comfortably stand, walk, and it was difficult to climb stairs. I tried to massage my hamstrings but they were too tender to tolerate it. So, I soaked in a hot tub and took some Motrin and Tylenol.

The following day was even worse. I was miserable. The pain and tightness increased. I paid the price for my pride, foolishness, and competitiveness. Soaking in a hot tub and medication made the pain barely bearable. It took almost two weeks before the acute pain and soreness resolved. The right hamstring was pain-free, but not my left. Now I had an almost constant deep aching pain in my left hamstring and it tightened up when I performed quick and forceful movements, such as jumping, squats, or a sprint on a cross-trainer. I swallowed my pride and made an appointment with my physical therapist. I felt foolish when I explained how I reinjured my hamstring.

This began my second round of intense therapy for my hamstring. I suffered a bad strain and it was preventable. At the end of a therapy session I finished off with this wonderful ice wrap. The ice soothed the chronic pain and the soreness from the exercises. Two months later I was still experiencing the dull aching pain in my left hamstring. I also had not recovered the flexibility I had before the injury, due to pain. I applied ice packs religiously and continued to progress my exercise under the watchful eye of my physical therapist and technician. Four months after my injury, and two months after starting therapy, I could resume wrestling practice. I was plagued, however with a persistent, deep ache in my left hamstring.

I was much more mindful of my body and did not let my pride override common sense. I warmed up thoroughly before a workout. If certain exercises or wrestling moves caused pain in my hamstring I stopped and modified what I was doing. I spent extra time to stretch at the end of practice. At home, nightly ice packs, regular massage with a foam roller, and Motrin and Tylenol became mainstays.

Eight months after my foolish over-use injury I still suffered from the deep aching in my left hamstring. It was most intense at night and some nights I would get up to take medication, because it either made it difficult to fall asleep or it would awaken me at night. My pride continued to exact a price. I discussed this ongoing pain with another colleague, the Director of the Pain Center. He, in turn, prescribed treatment with alternative medical providers, a massage therapist and a yoga therapist.

After my first session with the massage therapist, I felt better than I had in several months. It was an amazing shift. After a few months of therapy with these alternative medical providers, the deep ache in my left hamstring subsided and eventually resolved. Whew, it had been over ten months since the onset of my injury. Physical therapy twice weekly, a modified workout routine, limited wrestling practice, nightly ice packs, massage with a foam roller, medication, and alternative medical treatment. If only I had stopped practicing a foot sweep at the first twinge of soreness in my hamstrings! Prevention is so much better and easier than rehabilitation.

My brother Chris, a personal trainer, reminds me regularly, "Skip, train your body, not your ego." A fellow wrestler, he understands that my typical mindset is to over-train, which puts me at risk of over-use injuries, aggravating old injuries, and unnecessarily increasing the wear and tear on my body.

Prevention also applies to depression. The signs were there. I chose to disregard, misattribute their cause, or deny them. I was tough! "I'm a Soldier. I'm a man. I'm a wrestler!" Looking back, I understand that this was going on unconsciously. I battled through and "toughed out" demanding situations. That's what I had done all my life. Disrupted sleep, poor concentration, impaired memory, anxiety, blue mood, recurrent self-disparaging thoughts, emotional and social withdrawal, guilt, and shame are all hallmarks of depression. In retrospect, these symptoms were present to some degree the year before I finally sought care for depression. Yes, I was tough, but I could not tough it out against these relentless foes, and it was only after they became debilitating that I admitted I was depressed and finally sought care.

I've often wondered what my recovery would have looked like if I had sought help earlier. Even so, I had a marked improvement in my mood, sleep, cognition, sociability, emotional energy, and joy of life within the first six months of cognitive behavioral therapy and within four months of taking medication. However, it took over eighteen months before I felt close to my baseline state. Truth be told, I don't know if I will ever recover fully to my pre-illness state. My pride, denial, and stubbornness prevented me from seeking help sooner. Sound familiar? Unfortunately, I did not translate my preventable physical over-use injuries to the injuries caused by depression to my mind, soul, and body.

So, what does prevention of depression look like? It starts with an awareness of the status of your well-being. Are you optimistic, joyful, and experience a deep sense of gratitude? Are you mentally sharp? Do you exercise your mind? Can you focus, retain new information, and readily recall it? Is your self-talk positive, encouraging, and forgiving? Do your readily laugh when you read, see, or hear something funny? Do you look forward to devoting time to your passions? Are you sleeping well? Are you eating a nutritious diet in the right proportions? Are you engaged in regular exercise? Are you spending quality time with those you love most? Are you investing your time, talent, and treasure (resources) in a meaningful way? Do you commune with nature? Do you commune with God?

It's all too easy to disregard changes when you are struggling. It is important to keep tabs on your health and well-being. Stress is cumulative and takes its toll. Being aware of the stressors in your life is important. Likewise, it's important to consider the impact of these stressors. This can help you devise a "training plan" to deal with these stressors in a positive way. Let's face it, few of us, especially those of us of the male species, like to admit to struggles, fears, or failures. We are proud! We want to solve our own problems. I ignored the twinges of pain in my hamstrings due to my pride. I didn't stop and assess the consequences. My failure to either readjust my workout or discontinue it altogether resulted in a severe injury. I ignored the earliest signs of potential injury and foolishly pressed ahead, because I didn't want to be a whiner or a wimp. Now I tell myself, "Who cares what others think! I am going to take care of myself." I am now more aware and dedicated to take care of my body and my whole being.

Awareness and regular self-checkups are important. If you do not take time to do an inventory on a regular basis, it can be disastrous. Even if you only spend a few minutes before the start of your day to assess your overall status, priorities for the day, and anticipated obstacles, this can help you plan how to most effectively use your time and energy. Also, a few minutes spent at the end of your day to reassess your overall well-being, accomplishments, and the allocation of your time and energy on priorities can provide an important gauge to monitor your status. Disruptions to different aspects of your life can be expected from time to time. It is important to be aware of the impact of these disruptions. How do they impact your overall health and well-being? Awareness is predicated by self-reflection. The latter requires a regular investment of time.

You may be thinking, "I don't have time to do a regular inventory on my health and well-being." Remember, prevention is better than rehabilitation. Don't let your pride, stubbornness, or denial short-change you. To remain healthy and function optimally, you must invest time to measure and track your overall status. It's been said, "If you don't measure it, how do you know if you are winning?" If you are not aware of your overall status and its impact on your day-to-day functions, how can you work to prevent a crisis? If you recall, I was curled up behind a desk, asking, "Skip, what are you doing?" What if I had faithfully measured and tracked my overall health and well-being prior to getting to that point? As mentioned, the telltale signs of depression were present long before I was in crisis.

Let's review the telltale signs to closely monitor. You can rate these items on a 1-10 scale or in a graphic format. There are even some new "apps" that help you do this in a digital format. Check in with yourself and do a regular and honest inventory. If you see a progressive decline in several areas or the decline in one area has a marked impact on your day-to-day function, please seek help.

Ask yourself:

- Do I get adequate and restful sleep? Do I awaken feeling refreshed? Do I make
- sleep a priority?
- Do I eat nutritious meals in healthy proportions?
- Do I engage in daily exercise?
- How is my mood? Am I more blue, irritable and impatient than normal?
- Am I able to focus, learn and retain new material, and readily recall information?
- Are my most important relationships positive? Do I make them a priority?
- Do I spend time on and find my passions/hobbies enjoyable? Or, have I lost interest
- in them?
- Is my self-talk positive?
- Do I believe my life matters? Do I make a positive contribution?
- Is my energy level high?
- Do I have faith practices that I regularly spend time in?
- Am I joyful?
- Do I readily express gratitude?
- Do I commune with nature?
- Overall, how is my health and well-being?

A daily practice of spending a few minutes on a quick and brief inventory of your well-being, and 15–30 minutes weekly on a focused, honest, and quantitative inventory can prove to be invaluable. Don't leave your health and well-being to chance. Take charge. You owe it to yourself and to those you love and depend on you. Listen to your "body" and make wise adjustments to prevent further injury. Note, a decline in areas may be subtle, almost imperceptible, and go unnoticed until you are significantly impaired. It takes practice to become sensitized to your overall health and well-being. It takes time to track and measure key areas that can signal a change worth further exploration and consideration.

I recommend you begin with the "Big 3": sleep, nutrition, and exercise, combined with mood and your interest level in pursuing those things most important to you. A daily check-in as described above can help you make healthy and proactive adjustments accordingly. When you are in the throes of depression you may lack the emotional, mental, and physical energy to track these items. If so, I recommend you start monitoring sleep and mood. As you begin to recover, your increased energy will allow you to track more areas. Make it easy to succeed. Consider keeping a chart on your bedside table or on the kitchen table.

Life's demands can result in fatigue, preoccupation with these demands, and feeling overwhelmed. Wrestlers are familiar with what feeling overwhelmed is like as they juggle multiple disciplines and activities, such as losing and maintaining weight, arduous practices, and the ongoing responsibilities of school, relationships, and work. The discipline required to deal with these demands takes a Herculean effort. It often means saying no to "fun" things, such as attending a party, going out to eat with friends, or staying up late to watch a movie. It also means saying no to treats such as chocolate, ice cream, or pizza. When young wrestlers voice that they are feeling overwhelmed, I recommend they emphasize the basics: healthy nutrition, smart training, and adequate sleep. They must train themselves to avoid unnecessary stressors and develop healthy strategies—to manage what they can and to be in the best physical and mental condition possible to deal with unavoidable stress. A wise coach keeps tabs on his wrestlers and intervenes when he sees any of them struggling to cope. Without the watchful eye and appropriate intervention of a coach, some of these wrestlers falter on the mat, others contemplate quitting, and some walk away from wrestling altogether.

Sometimes a wrestler's strategy is to come out like a "ball-of-fire," attempting to quickly subdue his opponent. A wrestler may feel overwhelmed by this fast, skillful, and powerful opponent. Smart coaches prepare their wrestlers to withstand this initial firestorm and not play into the hands of their opponents. Coaches teach their wrestlers situational awareness, and how not to panic. It is amazing to watch a wrestler withstand a maelstrom at the beginning of a match by not losing his head. They employ strategies to slow the pace down, recompose themselves, and go on the attack. This can be accomplished by relying on the basics.

Coaches push their wrestlers to master basic techniques. My brother Chris and I were proponents of the basics. We were very predictable wrestlers. We laugh now, recalling how opponents knew what moves to expect from us and yet they couldn't overcome us. I recall wrestling and defeating Eric Wilfong, at the 1978 Rocky Mountain Regional AAU Championship Tournament. I knew Eric because a few years earlier I wrestled his brothers in Freestyle Wrestling Tournaments. After defeating Eric, his father told me with a grin, "Skip, we knew what you were going to throw, we just couldn't stop you."

The basics are essential on the wrestling mat and in the match of life. In life, it is important to identify when you face a maelstrom, to acknowledge its force, and stay cool. Don't panic. You can learn strategies to s-l-o-w the pace of life down, recompose yourself, and "go on the attack." I highlight how to do this later, especially in Chapter 14, "Get in the Zone," and Chapter 15, "Enjoy the Journey," where I discuss the importance of mindfulness.

Prevention trumps rehabilitation. Unfortunately, once we have suffered a severe injury, we are more vulnerable to re-injury. Consider my hamstring injury as a classic example of this. Wrestlers, like NFL players, suffer traumatic brain injuries, but it is the sport of football that leads the way with research, prevention, evaluation, and treatment. These multi-million-dollar NFL football players have the best surgeons, physical therapists, and other medical specialists at their beck and call, along with expensive and sophisticated protective equipment, and sideline physicians and trainers to assess them if they are injured. The NFL has learned that if one of their players is injured and not promptly assessed and removed from the game for further evaluation when indicated, this player is more susceptible to re-injury. More importantly, recurrent injuries can cause permanent damage. This is highlighted by the publicity of the effects of recurrent traumatic brain injuries (concussions). This also applies to mental health disorders, including depression. This is one more reason to monitor our status and adopt a healthier lifestyle to build more resilience in our lives to withstand the inevitable stresses we all face.

Lessons Learned

- Keep score to know if you are winning.
  - Quantify and track the most important aspects of your life.
  - If you begin to see a decrease in something important, you're "losing:" stop and assess why.
- If you are losing, go back to the basics:
  - Maintain your routines of exercise, healthy eating, and quality sleep.
  - Keep your cool—don't panic!
- If aspects of life begin to hurt, don't neglect the first twinges of discomfort—take inventory.
  - Pain tells you something is wrong; it may be minor, or it may be serious.
- Self-reflection is essential:
  - Requires time and space. Set aside time for it.
  - Discomfort is not always unhealthy; if we determine it is, it may be wise to consider other choices.
- Don't push recklessly on, with the expectation that your situation will improve without deliberate changes.

- Denial often allows the "injury" to progress, making it harder to recover.
    - Stop and ask, "What can I do to limit this pain?"
- Once you've suffered an injury, you're more vulnerable to re-injury.
- Do everything possible to recover from the original injury and to help prevent recurrent injury.
- Be willing to say, "No," or to ask, "Can I do something instead, or differently, because this is causing harm?"
- Don't let pride or concern about what others might think stymie your efforts of better self-care. Self-care is not selfish!
- Ask for help early. It may save you from lots of pain later.

CHAPTER 9

Get Your Head Up

"Get your head up. Head up. Get your head up!" If you attend a wrestling practice or match, you hear coaches shout out this instruction. If your head is down, you are vulnerable to your opponent's attacks. Whether on your feet or down on the mat, if your head is down you put yourself in danger. Inexperienced wrestlers are prone to this mistake.

When I coach, I instill in my wrestlers, "Where the head goes, the body will follow." Think of the situations in life when your head hangs down: when faced with fatigue, shame, loss, and grief. Body language reflects your physical status and emotions. When fatigued your body naturally tends to slump and your head hangs down. When you feel ashamed you struggle to hold your head up. When gripped by grief you also hang your head. Loss sucks the joy and energy out of life.

An adage says, "When you're winning, nothing hurts and when you're losing, everything hurts." At the end of a wrestling match, the body language reflects the winner and the loser. The winner stands tall, smiling, energized, head up, and chest out, waiting for the referee to raise his hand in victory. The loser stands slumped, fatigue and disappointment written on his face, and his head down. When you are in the depths of depression, listen for those in your life shouting encouraging things, like, "Get your head up. Head up. Get your head up!"

Depression also sucks the joy of life out of you. It leaves you discouraged, full of despair, and feeling a dreadful sense of defeat. Everything hurts. Ouch! It is hard to face life, standing tall, head up, chest out, and smiling, when you feel defeated. Motivation, energy, and creativity are depleted. You are in a survival mode, doing your best to make it through the day.

As a coach, you learn to put your arm around the shoulders of a defeated wrestler and speak a few words of encouragement. You tell them what they did well, or improved upon during the match. You also tell them, "Keep your chin up and get yourself ready for the next match." This is an essential task for every coach.

A coach points out what situation made their wrestler vulnerable during the match, and how to correct it. To punctuate their learning, the coach asks them to recreate the situation, and shows them how to properly wrestle through it. Then the wrestler must practice those winning moves several times under the coach's watchful eye. Committed wrestlers are always looking for ways to improve. Those who only dabble in the sport repeat the same mistakes, are unwilling to learn from their mistakes, and unwilling to listen to wise instruction. As with any endeavor, it takes commitment and determination to stick with something and to excel at it.

If you wrestle with depression, you similarly need "coaches" in your life. You need external voices that speak more loudly than the negative and toxic self-talk of defeat. My caring psychologist, Dr. Mike Perry, was one of my "depression coaches." Week in and week out, he confronted my negative sense of reality with a more objective viewpoint. He reminded me to recall why I became a physician and why I joined the Army. He explored and helped me affirm how I had been true to the sacred trusts of service as a physician and an Army Officer. More importantly, he helped me to see I had been true to loving and serving God and my family.

Likewise, my wife, children, extended family, church, and friends reminded me regularly of their love, concern, and appreciation. Over and over, they reminded me of the love, generosity, and service I demonstrated to them. Throughout our marriage my wife, Sherry, has been relentless in her support, encouragement, and kindness towards me. During the early months of my illness, she redoubled her efforts to show me TLC. I am so grateful because that's exactly the medicine I needed.

Sherry, my family, church, friends, and my psychologist and my primary care physician all told me in their own kind, gentle, and loving ways, "Skip, get your head up. Head up. Get your head up." Some days it was hard to get out of bed and face the prospect of a new day. But I was determined not to remain defeated. I began to allow the external voices of those who loved me and those who cared for me to echo in my mind and heart, and crowd out the negative self-talk that had dominated my thinking for months.

A major turning point in my recovery occurred six to eight weeks after I first sought help for my depression. My brother Chris called to excitedly tell me about a Bible study he had attended in Raleigh, North Carolina. Franklin Graham, a prominent conservative Christian leader and teacher had spoken about suffering. Suffering! Boy, did I know about suffering! It had been my constant companion, with little reprieve for several months. Chris shared how Franklin laid out a Biblical basis to understand suffering. Inhuman suffering was heaped upon Jesus Christ. Yet, He did not shirk it, but prayed, "Not my will, but thine be done." Why as American Christians steeped in Western Culture, do we think we will not have to suffer? As I pondered this conversation over the next few days, I began to ask myself why I felt I was entitled to deliverance from *my* suffering.

Deep down, I believed that suffering is inevitable, that I could not avoid it, and neither should I always expect to be delivered from its ravages. Yet, when faced with the stark reality of the relentless and daily profound suffering of my body, mind, and spirit, I yearned for relief. It was an epiphany to be reminded that suffering is a normal part of life. When I embraced the inevitability of suffering, my prayers changed. Instead of praying, "God, please deliver me from this pit," I began to pray, "God, what do you want me to learn from this suffering? How can I use this experience to help others?"

This change in perspective and, in turn, in focus, was pivotal to my recovery. Instead of trying to outwit, outrun, and out-pray suffering, I decided to embrace it. I looked into its dark, foreboding face and decided I could live a life of purpose, peace, and principle in the midst of suffering.

The self-disparaging dialogue that overwhelmed me in my darkness slowly began to give way to positive self-talk. I heeded the instruction of the many "coaches" in my life. Although sometimes I regressed, I began to raise my head, smile more, and even laugh. My *joie de vivre* was returning. I was no longer wallowing in constant defeat, but began to bask in small victories. I told Sherry, "I *am* going to get better! It is not always going to be like this." I envisioned myself well, and sensed I was climbing out of the mire I was stuck in, out of a deep, dark pit.

I began to replace my negative ruminations with heartfelt soothing and loving self-talk, such as: "I am God's beloved child; I am a kind, generous, and loving husband, father, and grandfather; My wife, children, and grandchildren love and appreciate me; I am a dedicated, determined, and accomplished U.S. Army Medical Corps Officer; I am a fine clinician and teacher." At first, I felt like a fraud—my words rang hollow. I'd think, "I want to believe this, but…." Over time, however, I began to embrace these words. My thoughts changed to, "Yes, this is who I am!" Eventually, I could say and even shout these affirmations out loud when I was alone. I once again knew this is who I was. "Yes, I am beloved, appreciated, and my sacrificial service and contributions matter!" Such words welled up from a grateful heart.

After many months, I again held my head up, chest out, a smile on my face, and a deep and renewed sense of gratitude and joy welled up within me. I did not get there on my own. I needed the help of many to remind me of my true value to them, God, and others. They were relentless in reminding me, "Skip, get your head up. Head up. Get your head up!" This made all the difference.

Earlier in this chapter, I discussed how body language mirrors your emotions. Did you know the converse is also true? Your emotions mirror your body language. An exciting and growing body of research shows you can influence how you feel by changing your body language. Your facial expressions, posture, and hand gestures can either help you to feel more confident and powerful, or weaker and more vulnerable. A smile makes you feel more energetic and optimistic. A frown makes you feel more tired and less optimistic. This, in part, is related to the release of endorphins when you smile. Smiling not only makes you feel better, it makes you healthier. Endorphins increase your immune system and give you a boost of energy. When you frown, you release more cortisol, "the stress hormone," and other chemicals that promote inflammation. Both are detrimental to our health and well-being. Unchecked, cortisol and inflammatory mediators lower immunity and promote the development of progression of many diseases, such as diabetes, cancer, and heart disease.

An expansive stance, a "power pose" like Superman, with feet spread, chest out, hands on hips, and head up with a confident smile translates into a surge of testosterone and lowers cortisol. A surge of testosterone increases your energy, confidence, relaxation, improves your cognition, and enhances your creativity. In short, it makes you feel like a winner and makes you more attractive to others. In contrast, assume a slouched posture, shoulders rounded, head down, a frown or fearful look on your face, and your hands clasped in front of you. The result? Lower testosterone and higher cortisol levels, which then results in feeling more anxious, less able to analyze, formulate, and recall information, and also less creative, energetic, confident, and attractive. This weakened state also lowers immunity and increases one's risk of developing various diseases.

If you want to feel more like a winner, start "acting" more like a winner. Stand up straight and tall, spread your feet, stick your chest out, pull your shoulders back, and lift your head up with a great *big* smile. Try it. You'll like it.

Lessons Learned

- When wrestling with depression, you need the voices of many "coaches" in your life to remind you, "Get your head up!"
- Practice, practice, practice to keep your head up.
- Find several ways to lift your head up and counter negative self-talk; recollect and list:
  - Those who unconditionally love you.
  - Those willing and ready to help you pursue health and well-being.
  - Your significant contributions.

  - The people and things in life you are most grateful for.
- Create a book of dreams and aspirations.
  - Envision the joy, challenge, and satisfaction when you accomplish them.
  - Let these dreams and aspirations help propel you forward.
  - Embrace your future and envision yourself well, whole, and restored with a newfound sense of purpose.
- Take time to reminisce and enjoy happier times.
  - Relish old photographs, memorable videos, letters, cards, mementos, plaques, and awards.
  - Allow yourself to laugh, give thanks, and even cry.
  - Many men have trouble crying; tears can help wash away depression's darkness, despair, and destruction.
- Employ positive affirmations; be relentless to counteract negative self-talk:
  - Talk to yourself in a loving, kind, gentle manner, how you speak to a child.
  - Remember, self-care, is not selfish!
- Use Body Language to your advantage:
  - A weak, contracted posture with your head down, weakens you (it's like kryptonite to Superman!).

- Use positive body language to bolster your confidence, energy, creativity, and sense of control (Superman sure had something going for him).
    - You have heard the adage, "Fake it until you make it." Body language experts tell you, "Fake it until you feel it."

One of the leading experts in the study and application of body language is Vanessa Van Edwards. You can find her enlightening and entertaining resources on YouTube or at *Science of people.*

CHAPTER 10

No Ifs, Ands, or Buts!

"I wish I was as good as you." I heard many younger wrestlers, and even some of my peers tell me this during high school. I rode a wave of success: I won several state freestyle wrestling tournaments; I placed in two national freestyle wrestling tournaments; I defeated numerous state champions; I intimidated wrestlers when I stepped on the mat to face them. This had not always been the case. I wrestled two full seasons before I won my first wrestling match, so when I began winning regularly, I basked in the fruits of my labor.

When I heard those words, "I wish I was as good as you," I thought, *No you don't, because you're not willing to pay the price.* That may sound harsh, but it's the truth. Being good enough to win meant saying no to many other things and to train instead: lifting weights three times a week; getting up early to run 2–3 miles in all kinds of weather, or alternatively one mile as fast as possible; skipping rope, and performing agility drills, chin-ups, push-ups, sit-ups daily; sprints, especially the dreaded 440-yard intervals; practicing on the mats at every opportunity; attending summer camps to improve and learn new techniques, and so on. This was my training regimen throughout my high school career.

Sacrifice, focus, and grit were my constant companions. I determined not to have any regrets when I finished my wrestling career. As we say in wrestling, "I was going to leave it all on the mat!" I decided that "if, and, or but" were not acceptable. When I faced a defeat, I picked myself up, analyzed my loss, and dedicated myself to improve. I trained to be better than anyone else, even on an off day. I did not like to lose! In fact, I replayed some of my most stinging defeats over in my mind hundreds of times, envisioning how I'd wrestle those opponents differently, if given the opportunity.

Fast-forward to February 2012. My eighteen-year old son Joey, and my wife, Sherry, and I, watched the Georgia State High School Wrestling Tournament Finals. Joey, a very talented and dedicated wrestler, with well over one hundred victories, was injured and ill, and eliminated from the tournament. In between matches, we talked about the Veteran Freestyle Wrestling National Championship Tournament scheduled for early May. I told Joey, "I want to compete. Will you train with me?" "OK, Dad," he agreed, "but you're going to have to do what I tell you."

My fitness level was high, but that's not enough to effectively compete. Joey and I wrestled at least three times a week. I lifted weights on alternate days. I performed high intensity circuit routines or sprints on the cross-trainer to improve my anaerobic capacity. I took my chin-up bar to my office and worked up to several sets of chin-ups each day. I skipped rope and performed agility drills. I awakened fifteen minutes earlier to perform a short morning workout to complement my intense evening routine. My body ached, especially after wrestling practice.

Many nights I came home and told my wife, "I'm going to soak in a hot tub." Later I would sit on the couch with ice packs on various aching joints—shoulders, elbows, wrists, hands, and knees. I spent extra time stretching and massaging my sore muscles with a foam roller. My wife teased me, asking, "Don't you think you've had enough, old man?" To which I quickly retorted, "No, I haven't!" When my alarm sounded and my feet hit the floor, I was painfully aware of sore and tight muscles.

Slowly, over the next six weeks, I could feel my body becoming "wrestling tough." I exerted myself more easily. My endurance, strength, anaerobic capacity, speed, and coordination on the mat improved. I recovered from workouts more quickly. The day eventually arrived when I said to myself, "I'm feeling good," during my morning workout. I thought, "Son, you better bring your A-game tonight, because the old man is feeling really good!" Joey was a terrific training partner, coach, trainer, and manager. He prepared me well. No ifs, ands, or buts.

On May 4th, we arose at 5 AM to leave early and drive sixty-five miles to the Atlanta International Airport for a 9:30 AM flight to Tucson, Arizona. Or, so I thought. At the ticket counter I discovered we were not booked on the flight: I had failed to confirm that my payment was completed when I booked our fight weeks before, and it turned out it wasn't! Yikes. The flight was over-booked. Joey was alarmed and asked, "Dad, what are we going to do? Dad, what are we going to do?" I calmly replied, "We're going to be alright. I am going to get us on a different flight."

I regrouped and placed a call the American Express Concierge Service. Several minutes later I was speaking to a Travel Agent. I explained I needed to travel to Tucson, Arizona. The arrival time of the original flight I planned on, arrived in Tucson at approximately 2:30 PM, allowing plenty of time to get settled in our hotel, locate the competition venue, and prepare for the weigh-in and medical check for Veterans Freestyle competitors scheduled from 6-8 PM. I booked a later flight, at a much higher cost, scheduled to arrive in Phoenix at approximately 2:30 PM. We had to deplane, get our bags, rent a car, and after a ninety-minute drive to Tucson we would have a thirty-minute cushion before weigh-in. Thus, began the first leg of our journey.

We boarded and took off without a hitch. Forty minutes into the flight a warning light came on and the captain alerted us that he and his co-pilot were performing their normal checklist and expected to correct the issue. Ten minutes later the captain informed us the warning light remained on, so we were going to land in Mississippi. We landed with the expectation to be on the ground for less than an hour. A maintenance worker was arriving on the next flight. The hours ticked by. Meanwhile, Joey was even more alarmed, "Dad, you're going to miss weigh-in. What are you going to do?" I explained, "I called the meet director to request a late weigh-in, if I don't arrive in time." I refused to get upset. I had worked too hard to allow this to disrupt my mindset. I was going to compete. No, ifs, ands, or buts!

Unable to reach the meet director directly, I left three messages, explaining my dilemma in detail on the last message. We left Mississippi at approximately 7 PM, were diverted to Houston, and boarded a 10:30 PM flight to Phoenix. As we boarded, the meet director called back and I explained our situation again to him. He readily agreed to an early morning weigh-in and medical check. This put me at a distinct disadvantage, since other competitors had ample time to rehydrate and eat a hearty supper. I, however, would not be able to check my weight before weigh-in. This meant very limited fluids and a strict avoidance of anything salty to avoid water retention. We landed in Phoenix well after 11 PM. We had been awake since 3 AM Mountain Standard Time. We collected our baggage, headed to car rental, and were on the road by midnight. We checked into our hotel at 1:30 AM, 3:30 AM our time. I awakened after a few hours of sleep. Unable to fall back asleep I arose, dressed, and sought out the wrestling venue. I returned, shaved, put my wrestling singlet on under my sweat suit, and headed to weigh-in. I was the only Veteran wrestler among a few hundred high school wrestlers. I registered, cleared my medical check, and weighed in. No problem. Now it was time to prepare to compete. After a light breakfast I let my food settle for an hour, and headed to the arena to warm up.

I wrestled hard and won the 58-kilogram National Veterans Freestyle Championship in the oldest age group. No ifs, ands, or buts! I refused to be deterred, discouraged, or dissuaded that I'd compete. I was exhilarated profoundly and satisfied when I posed for a picture with Joey, holding my National Championship plaque. We did it! Joey later asked me, "Dad, was it worth it? All that training? All those ice packs?" Without hesitation I replied, "Yes, son, it was worth it!"

No Ifs, Ands, or Buts!

May 5, 2012 Tucson, Arizona. 58-kilogram National Veterans Freestyle Champion. My son Joey and I savor success. Joey was my trainer, manager, coach, and training partner. (Don't be fooled, my son is taller, if not for a step I stood on).

These lessons of determination, dedication, and discipline served me well as I grappled with depression. Depression sucked the life out of me. To review, I struggled with: blue mood, anxiousness, shame, guilt, and a loss of confidence and self-worth; depleted energy, motivation, and focus; social withdrawal and a sense of being isolated from God and others; disturbed sleep and a loss of interest in sex or other passions; fear of the future and a lack of joy and purpose.

Eventually, I had a visceral reaction, saying, "No, I'm not going to give in to despair! It is not going to defeat me. I'm going to get better." I said this through tears. Many days I felt I was hanging on by my fingernails. I drew strength and encouragement from past experiences as a wrestler. As a young wrestler, I persisted in my dream to be a champion in the face of defeat after defeat. A year of wrestling without one win would've demoralized most wrestlers, much less two years. I persisted and picked myself up after each painful loss and determined to work even harder. I envisioned myself a winner long before I won. I visualized shaking my opponent's hand and having my arm raised in victory, and the satisfaction and pride of standing atop the podium to accept the gold medal. I now realize these same lessons and practices employed in wrestling served me well in my recovery.

"I'm going to get better!" Saying these words out loud and to my wife Sherry was a key step in my recovery. The tiniest flicker of hope arose in my soul. No matter what, I was going to get better. I drew upon years of competition and training. I faced and overcame defeat at the hands of powerful and crafty wrestlers. I succeeded in the face of troublesome situations. Depression had me on my back, but I was determined not to stay there. Where to start?

Back to the basics. I recommitted myself to eat a healthy diet, daily exercise, and a strict attention to sleep hygiene. Of the three, sleep remained the most elusive. Improvements were slow and stuttering, but as my mood improved, so did my sleep. I experienced fewer nights feeling "tired but wired," in the words of sleep guru, Shawn Stevenson, unable to fall asleep. Episodes of waking up in the middle of the night, unable to get back to sleep decreased. I now awakened more often feeling refreshed and rested. As my depression lifted, I told others, "I don't know if my sleep is improved because my mood improved, or my mood improved because my sleep improved." In retrospect I believe both are true, and go hand-in-hand.

Spending time in the sunshine once again became part of my daily routine. I looked forward to a walk or sitting out on my patio enjoying the wondrous warming sensation of sunlight and marveling at the sights, sounds, and smells of nature. The simple practice of daily exposure to sunlight helped reset my circadian rhythms, boost my mood, and improve my sleep.

I turned my attention to the "BIG D" and "BIG E" too: *Diet* and *Exercise*. I increased my already ample portions of fresh fruits and vegetables, with an emphasis on the latter. I ate more foods rich in omega-3 oils, including fish, almonds, walnuts, and avocados. I supplemented my diet with fish oil capsules. I also modified my exercise routines.

Some mornings I went for a walk shortly after I awakened. I incorporated yoga, more stretching, and alternating days of heavy resistance training with days of aerobic exercise. For good measure, I eventually included a weekly session of high intensity circuit training, sometimes referred to as HIIT, high intensity interval training. Yoga soothed my mind and body. I became more attentive to my body and modified my workouts to allow my body time to recover between workouts. Note, the progression in exercise routines was slow and deliberate. I sought to heed the advice of my brother Chris, who said, "Skip, train your body, not your ego." In my case, it was just as important to my mind and mood to exercise wisely as it was for my body. Improvements in mood, sleep, and cognition both encouraged and spurred me on to persevere with a healthy diet, regular and varied exercise, and fastidious attention to sleep hygiene.

I still experienced nights when I either could not fall asleep or awakened and couldn't fall asleep again. Such nights no longer caused the dread and deep frustration that they had before. I accepted that these were blips on the radar and were not going to plague me night after night. I felt assured I was going to enjoy my day and sleep well the following night. The improvement in mood also translated into a renewed enjoyment of social situations. Rather than avoid situations, I began to accept invitations and look forward to outings. This, in turn, prompted me to enlist the help and support of others in my recovery. Productive, enjoyable, and supportive interactions were an additional boost to my mood and my confidence, which took a beating during the dark days of depression.

The axiom I mentioned before, "When you're losing, everything hurts and when you're winning, nothing hurts," was in effect in my life. Now, instead of the despair and pain in so many aspects of my life, I experienced more hope and peace. As the saying goes, "Nothing succeeds like success."

Lessons Learned

- Decide in the core of your being that you're not going to remain beat down, beat up, and battle weary.

- Determine "I am going to get better!"
- Begin to take steps, no matter how small, today.
- Remember, "Say it until you feel it."
- Envision yourself as healthy, hopeful and happy.
- Commit to do whatever it takes to regain your health—no ifs, ands, or buts!
- Draw upon the lessons of perseverance, determination, and sacrifice forged in the successes and failures in the past.
    - Use them to steel you and as a springboard.
- Recommit to the basics: a healthy diet, regular and refreshing exercise, and strict attention to sleep hygiene.
- If you can only muster enough energy and motivation to address one of the basics, devote your efforts to first improve your sleep hygiene.
    - Improvements in sleep will pay dividends in mood, cognition, energy, and an overall sense of health and well-being.
- Enjoy 30 minutes daily of sun exposure to help reset and maintain a healthy circadian rhythm.
    - Spending time in the sun between 8 and 10 AM is especially helpful.
- Celebrate small successes—Success is contagious and it builds on itself.
    - Remember, "Nothing succeeds like success."

- Gain momentum from success and improvements to make additional changes.
    - Small changes add up over time: one change a week, if sustained, can mean profound changes over time.
- Don't become discouraged if progress is slow, stuttering, and setbacks occur: this is normal.
    - See yourself as a hero on a quest to recover from depression, and restore the fortunes of your health for a lifetime.
- When setbacks occur, return to the basics.
    - The more you practice, the easier it becomes.
    - Sometimes we need an arm around our shoulders and words of encouragement to keep us fighting in the match of life.
- Enlist the help of loving, kind, and supportive individuals who will, "speak the truth in love" when you get off-track, and celebrate your successes.
- A diet rich in a variety of fresh fruits and vegetables and ample amounts of omega-3s are a boon to mood, cognition, and overall health.
- Be kind to your body and get moving!
- Regular exercise also improves mood, cognition, and overall health and well-being.

- Strict attention to the basics of nutrition, regular and varied exercise, and strict sleep hygiene is simple, but often under-rated and neglected.
- Ask from time to time, "Have I allowed unhealthy habits to creep in and impact my attention and appreciation of the basics?" If so, recommit to an honest reassessment and devise a "training plan" to shore up the basics.

CHAPTER 11

Avoid Toxins: Resentment, Unforgiveness, and Regret

Wrestling is a sport that requires incredible discipline. As in other sports, wrestlers train to improve their strength, explosiveness, agility, balance, flexibility, endurance, and anaerobic capacity. They work diligently to hone their offensive and defensive skills. They are ardent students of the strengths and weaknesses of opponents. They review video-recorded matches of opponents to look for an edge. They use a variety of methods to calm, focus, and put themselves in a positive frame of mind before a match. The best and most successful wrestlers do not leave their diet to chance. They are meticulous about what they eat and drink. Remember, wrestlers compete at a specific weight class. Top wrestlers avoid toxins such as alcohol, tobacco, and illicit substances. Everything they do is with the end in mind, to optimize their performance and peak at the appropriate time.

Today, Olympic wrestlers have sports psychologists, strength and conditioning coaches, dietitians, trainers, and even masseuses, chiropractors, and acupuncturists, along with physicians readily available to assist them. Some of these disciplines were only used in a rudimentary way, if at all, in the 1970's.

I trained hard physically. I absolutely avoided alcohol, tobacco, and illicit substances. But I did not understand all the components that can contribute to optimal performance. I was frustrated by my inconsistent performance. I'd defeat a tough opponent one week, only to tie or lose to another the following week. Sometimes the ties or losses were to lesser opponents. How was I going to turn this around? After four years of wrestling, however, I started to understand the importance of mental preparation and toughness if I wanted to be more consistent and successful.

A change occurred after the Colorado State Wrestling Tournament in my junior year of high school. I defeated some very talented and tough wrestlers and I also lost two matches. One of these was very closely contested. In the other, I was overpowered. I was not prepared for the barrage a much stronger wrestler threw at me. In both cases, my mental preparation and toughness were not up to par. As a result, I failed to make the award stand. This did not sit well with me. The wrestlers I lost to placed 2nd and 4th. I knew I had to improve to beat such opponents.

I also suffered a shoulder injury in my final match of this tournament because I was not mentally prepared, and had to modify my training preparing for the upcoming Freestyle Wrestling season. In the following weeks, I took time to reflect on my performance at the state tournament. I pondered, "What more do I need to do to win at a higher level?" I also asked, "What changes do I have to make?" Consider, my readers, that you are competing in a grueling three-day tournament and each opponent you face is depression, in one form or another. Each is relentless, merciless, and enjoys inflicting pain. How can you improve your mental preparation and toughness? What steps can you take to make yourself less vulnerable to the taunts, harassment, and put-downs of these crafty opponents?

With the Freestyle Wrestling season on the horizon, I was determined to be better prepared. My physical conditioning was outstanding and I prided myself in being able to sustain a faster and more intense pace than most any other opponent. I was well coached and I had a very tough training partner, my friend and teammate, Russ Waag. We pushed each other in practice. Neither of us liked to yield even one point to the other.

As I gradually realized that I had to improve my mental preparation and toughness, I simultaneously read and heard about the exploits of Dan Gable, who was the face of the 1972 United States Olympic Freestyle Wrestling Team. Dan's physical and mental prowess on the wrestling mat was legendary. Dan enjoyed victory at all levels of wrestling: junior high, high school, Division 1 College, and the most prestigious national and international Freestyle Wrestling tournaments. Dan also had the distinction of an undefeated record until his last match in college. After he recovered from this devastating loss, he regrouped, reassessed, and resolved not to lose again.

Dan trained like a madman on a life-or-death mission. Nothing was going to deter him from an Olympic Gold Medal. He was determined to "break" his opponents, both physically and mentally. Dan defeated all opponents in the toughest tournaments around the globe. The Russian Wrestling Federation vowed to find a wrestler to defeat him at the Olympic Games. Instead, Dan defeated every opponent, including the Russian he faced, in dominant fashion and on the world's biggest stage of wrestling, the Olympic Games. He was not only undefeated, but also unscored upon. Dan Gable was the epitome of a wrestler's wrestler.

So, mental preparation. Where to start? Sports psychology was in its infancy and there was little readily available information. I realized I needed two critical elements. First, I needed to develop a routine to help me to remain calm, focused, and fully confident when I stepped on the mat to compete. Second, I needed to improve my mental focus and toughness during a match. I started to incorporate relaxation techniques, including deep breathing and progressive muscle relaxation, coupled with visualization. I visualized myself successfully executing move after move against my toughest opponents, including those who defeated me in the past. I imagined the sights, sounds, smells, and other sensations of a hard-fought match. I would relish the sensation of my hand raised in victory and the satisfaction and pride standing atop the podium accepting the gold medal.

I flooded my mind with positive images and positive thoughts. I chose to concentrate on my goals and not rehash defeats over and over. I worked diligently and daily to improve my mental toughness. As with all other new skills it took repeated practice to learn and incorporate these new mental skills.

I practiced these techniques before matches and before bedtime. It took repeated practice to learn to relax, focus, and "say" and listen only to positive statements in my mind. I trained hard and employed these mental disciplines diligently. This was the turning point. My mental training helped me to focus, calm my jittery nerves, and step out on the mat with more confidence. I rarely suffered a mental lapse. One of the crucial elements that separates great wrestlers from good wrestlers is their mental preparation and mental toughness. My mental training program helped me to stay in the moment, to adjust, and recover from mistakes more easily during competition. I enjoyed an amazing winning streak. I left multiple state champions in my wake during the Freestyle Wrestling season. The major difference in my training was my mental preparation and it served me well.

When faced with depression you may battle against the mental toxins of resentment, unforgiveness, and regret. Learning to avoid the mental toxins that negatively impacted my wrestling performance, and to focus on the positive elements crucial to my top performance, were just as critical in my battle with the powerful and relentless foe of depression.

One thing these three mental toxins have in common is that they root you in the past. I tell others when they are stuck in the past, "If you continue to look in the rearview mirror, you cannot see what is in front of you." These toxins can keep you stuck and impede your recovery. Resentment can be very sneaky. You may even resent the good health and well-being of family and friends. When I struggled to get even a few hours of uninterrupted sleep, and spent the night up and down, and tossing and turning, I feared I was disturbing my wife. I was also envious and even a bit resentful of her soft, sonorous breathing and peaceful state. I was "tired and wired," so sleep eluded me. As you know by now, I dreaded nighttime. As bedtime approached, I began to worry that I would not be able to either fall asleep or stay asleep. This only added to my bedtime angst. Depression amplified my negative emotions.

In the writing of this book, I went back and read entries of my journal when I was sinking into depression. I do not recall reading these entries since I had written them. The resentment due to perceived slights and the lack of an expression of gratitude from others exudes from these entries. Day after day, I rehashed these events. I ask, "Why can they not send a card or pick up the phone to say thanks?" "I've traveled several hours on various occasions to visit him, and after my surgery, he calls and asks me if I would travel three hours away to have supper? Then, when he returns home and travels through my city, he doesn't even bother to stop and see me? What's wrong with this picture?" "I've supported his ministry for years, so why haven't I ever received even a short note of thanks?" On and on these entries went. I am a very generous person by nature. I like to give and support causes I believe in. I enjoy encouraging and visiting others and recognized that my station in life allowed me more flexibility to travel as my children grew older and left the home. Yet, I was now drowning in resentment, bitterness, and unforgiveness. I was the caregiver and always had been! Now I needed care and struggled to admit this to others, much less to ask for it. Why could they not see this? I'd just undergone my second surgery in three months, and eventually my third in less than seven months.

When I was well, I generally could face, acknowledge, and dispense with most negative emotions quickly. This was not the case when I was depressed. Self-disparaging thoughts and feelings attacked me over and over. As my depression worsened, so did the relentless barrage of negative thoughts and emotions, which spilled over onto others. I was mired in a deep pit of discouragement, despair, and defeat.

Resenting my wife's peaceful sleep served no useful purpose for me. It was not helpful to ask myself over and over, "Why can't I get some sleep like Sherry?" or "Why me? Why me? Why me?" Other perceived slights were amplified and I replayed them over and over in my mind. Rather than think the best of others, I felt disregarded, disrespected, and quickly dismissed. I relived these images in my mind relentlessly and found it incredibly difficult to stop them.

None of this was conducive to improving my sleep or my mood. Once I sought help and began therapy, I became determined to face the resentment I harbored in my heart and mind, to counter my resentment with positive cogitations and self-talk, to more objectively look at situations, and to not immediately assume the worst of others. My therapist, Dr. Perry, was instrumental in this process. With his help, instead of trying to deny and push away the ugly ruminations and visceral reactions of resentment, I allowed myself to consciously experience all that the resentment evoked.

Once I was willing to acknowledge it, I could then ask myself, "What can I do to deal with my resentment?" I also asked, "Are there others I harbor resentment toward?" I had to go on the offensive, not simply stay defensive to counter these relentless foes. Instead, I listed the many wonderful traits of my wife and gave thanks for these. I silently recounted the many blessings in my life and gave thanks. I also rehearsed memorized Bible verses in my mind. When I arose from bed because I was unable to fall asleep, I sat on the couch and whispered the many things I was grateful for. I wrote lists of these same things in my journal. I quoted Scripture. Changing my mindset was not easy.

Unforgiveness is another toxin I had to confront, after realizing how much I replayed certain painful events over and over in my mind. Typically, these events involved others whom I felt were unkind, unjust, and failed to show understanding. I came to realize that my replay of these events and the emotions they provoked were a signal that I harbored unforgiveness. In some cases, it meant humbling myself and asking the people involved for forgiveness. In other cases, when I was unable to locate and contact individuals, I made a conscious decision to forgive. When the negative thoughts and feelings crept back in, I would go through the conscious process to forgive others, again. Sometimes I had to repeat this process several times. I have come to learn that forgiveness is a decision I make, not an emotion I experience. I tell myself, "I choose to forgive!"

I also had to learn to forgive myself. When I relived mistakes, failures, and poor decisions, I recognized this as a cue to forgive myself. I was, and am, my harshest critic, although now I try to speak to myself with kindness, respect, and patience (perhaps you too are your harshest critic.) Once again, I had to look at the harmful thoughts and emotions that accompanied my unforgiveness towards myself in order to deal with them in a conscious and purposeful manner. I was determined, however, to rid myself of the negative effects of unforgiveness. I chose to be kinder, gentler, and more loving toward myself. Life with its inevitable difficulties is hard enough to navigate without the self-imposed burdens of unforgiveness toward others and oneself.

Regret is also a powerful toxin. It has an unmistakable way of gluing you to past mistakes, failures, and unfulfilled longings. My father died suddenly when I was 13 years old. I felt guilt and regret that I did not call and speak to him in the weeks before his death. I struggled with this regret for some time. I finally decided that I was going to learn from this painful experience. I vowed to myself that I would take advantage of every opportunity to tell those most dear to me that I love them.

"I love you!" These have been words of healing and restoration for me. Rarely do I leave home without saying them to my wife Sherry, or end a conversation with my children, grandchildren, mother, siblings, other family members, or close friends, without uttering a heartfelt, "I love you!"

In February 1973, I lost the 112-pound finals at the Colorado AAA High School Wrestling Tournament, 2–1. I lost by two seconds of riding time to Matt Martinez from Greeley West High School. Over the years I relived this match hundreds, even thousands of times, before I could put it to rest. After a scoreless first period, frustrated by any attempt to attack his legs for a takedown, riding time was awarded to Matt in the second period when he was in the top position and maintained control for a full minute. He kept me down on the mat for a bit longer than a minute before I managed to escape. The remainder of the period I could not penetrate his defense to attempt, much less secure a takedown. In the third period, he escaped quickly, preserving his riding time. Matt wrestled a very intentional, well-planned match, never getting out of position to give me an opportunity to attack for a takedown.

For many years I felt as though I had failed myself, my family, my team, my coach, and my school. Five years of sacrifice that hinged on two seconds. "What if I did this? Or, how about this? I should've tried something else. I could've attempted…." On and on it went over the years. Sometime in my early thirties I was finally able to put that match into perspective, give thanks for the lessons it taught me, dust off and relish the great high school career I enjoyed, and recall the camaraderie I enjoyed with this fellow warrior and his tactical prowess. I determined I was not going to live a life of "should've, could've, and would've."

I now understand these sentiments are the voice of toxic regret.

As I contended with depression, I also grappled with regrets such as, "Skip, why didn't you seek help sooner?" and, "What would have happened if you dealt with the stress in your life more effectively?" These thoughts piled on to the negative ruminations I struggled with on a daily basis. I began to work through many regrets. This required that I acknowledge them, accept them for what they were, and actively choose to let go of them. I told myself, "I cannot change the past. I can live today to the best of my ability. I can choose to be grateful. I will concentrate on the blessings in my life." Banishing "would've, could've and should've" was no easy task. I had to retrain my mindset.

I became more aware of negative reflections that accompanied resentment, unforgiveness, and regret. I became more adept in countering these cogitations and emotions. I became intolerant of self-pity. I refused to listen to thoughts such as, "It's not fair," "Why me?" and, "What am I going to do?" I determined I was not going to continue to wring my hands in despair. It was time to fight back. Slowly I gained ground and began to experience success. Sometimes I struggled to believe my thoughts and words were true. As I persisted, my thoughts and words became more positive. This, in turn, increased my confidence and sense of success. As I experienced more confidence and success, my thoughts and words became increasingly more positive and heartfelt. I worked diligently to retrain my mind and slowly realized success.

Lessons Learned

- Resentment, unforgiveness, and regret tie us down to the past.
- Depression poisons your mind with negativity and colors everything in your life with darkness.
    - Unless countered, negative thoughts and emotions of depression are amplified and add to the discouragement, despair, and sense of defeat.
- Negativity is not conducive to health and well-being; health and wholeness are promoted by a shift in thinking and self-talk.
- Confront the toxins of resentment, unforgiveness, and regret.
    - Decide to look them fully in the face, evaluate the validity of these feelings, and address them.
- Resentment poisons one's mind and relationships.
    - It causes us to think the worst of others and question their motives. Awareness of negative thoughts and emotions allows us to deal with and replace them with positive and loving thoughts, and eventually positive and loving emotions.
- Past hurts from perceived slights, disregard, and disrespect loom larger and more pervasive in the face of depression, and promote unforgiveness.
    - Choose to forgive others; it gets easier over time!
    - Regret serves no useful purpose, except, perhaps, to make positive changes in your life.

- Learn from mistakes and poor choices and avoid the trap of "would've, could've, and should've."
- Forgive yourself and enjoy the freedom from this toxin.

- It is hard to be negative if you express gratitude.
  - In the depths of depression, this may seem monumental.
  - Consider all the simple things in your life and choose to express gratitude for them. Make it easy to set yourself up for success.
- Practice, practice, practice!
  - It takes time to deal with the entrenched and powerful foes of resentment, unforgiveness, and regret.
  - Repeated practice will help to cut these "tough guys" down to size.
- Choose to start today to retrain your mind.
  - You will not only feel better and function better, but you will enjoy and newfound freedom.
  - Try it; you'll like it!

CHAPTER 12

"Thanks Coach! I Needed That!"

I had not seen my first wrestling coach, John Gregerson, for over 20 years. Coach Gregerson coached me from 1968-70, and later coached my brothers, Frank, Mark, Duke, and Chris at Everitt Junior High, in Wheat Ridge, Colorado, a Denver suburb. I had last seen him at the 1994 NCAA Division 1 Wrestling Championship hosted by the University of North Carolina. In November 2015, my son Joey invited me to attend the Denver Broncos versus Kansas City Chiefs game, being played in the Mile High City. The day before the football game, Coach picked me up at my mother's house and we went to lunch. It was a real treat to catch up.

Years had passed since our last meeting, but we felt right at home. We chatted about our wives, children, grandchildren, wrestling, highlights of the intervening years since our last meeting, and dreams for the future. I was now on a first name basis with my coach, and we shared a profound, unspoken respect for one another. Before we parted I said, "I love you, John," and he replied in kind. A powerful bond is built between athletes and their coaches.

Coach Gregerson taught me the basics of wrestling, oversaw practices, gave advice on mat strategy, encouraged me in the face of defeat after defeat, and pushed me farther beyond physical and mental limits I had ever known I could go. Some of our drills in practices included situational wrestling, during which we were placed in situations we commonly faced during a wrestling match. Often, one wrestler was designated to be leading by one or two points. The other wrestler had to score to win.

The whistle blew and we grappled furiously for 15–30 seconds, then switched roles. We repeated this scenario with different situations for several minutes. We were spent, but then came the conditioning drills. We could count on set after set of burpees. I am convinced that the burpee was devised to either build you up physically or break you mentally, or both. Let me describe this tortuous exercise. Stand up, feet a little wider than shoulder width, squat down with hands on the floor between your feet, thrust your legs behind you in a push-up position, perform a pushup, return to the squat position, and stand up. Count "One!" Repeat for a total of ten and that's one set. Repeat several sets. We continued until coach determined we were finished.

Coach Gregerson turned up the heat—figuratively and literally. He turned the thermostat way up and pushed us hard. As practice progressed the walls of the gym would sweat as our sweat and moist breath condensed. We tried not to think ahead to the conditioning that awaited us at the end of practice. A wise coach learns how to push their wrestlers past their self-imposed and self-perceived limitations, mentally, physically, and emotionally. Coach Gregerson was a master at pushing his wrestlers to overcome these barriers.

You may recall I was beat down, beat up, and bogged down in negativity before I finally admitted I was depressed and reached out for help. Lieutenant Colonel Mike Perry, my therapist, served as both coach and counselor. At our first visit, he took time to start to get to know me, familiarize himself with my background, and explore my symptoms. He proceeded with tact, kindness, and compassion. From that first visit, "Coach Mike" began to counter my negative thinking. He pushed me to examine these negative thoughts more objectively. Mike subtly engaged me in some "warm-up" exercises, and gave me "training exercises" to practice before my next appointment to provide leverage to help counter my negative persuasions.

An experienced coach stands back and sees a bigger picture. By looking through a wide-angle lens, he spots potential problems and readily assesses the level of skill and confidence of his wrestler, while simultaneously devising a training program to address these issues. Week after week, Dr. Perry made me face my fears, doubts, and anxieties. He was firm, consistent, and sincerely concerned with my recovery. He encouraged and assured me that I was going to get better. Mike also pointed out and celebrated small successes. He was one of my staunchest cheerleaders. During this time, we developed a mutual respect, appreciation, and friendship. Thanks, Coach! I needed that!

An experienced and concerned coach is also an ardent student of his athletes and learns what best motivates each of them. Some wrestlers respond best to encouragement and readily accept the recommendation and guidance of their coach. Others require a firmer hand and an "in-your-face" approach. I fall into the former category. I am one of those wrestlers that is intrinsically motivated and I did not need a heavy-handed approach to do my best. On occasion, however, I did need a wake-up call.

One such time was my senior year of high school, during the quarterfinals of the Colorado State Tournament in 1973, wrestling Bobby Lucero from Montrose High School. I was in a daze for most of the match, but managed to score at the end of the match to send it into overtime. During the short break before overtime started, I was in my corner and my coach "talked" to me. Truthfully, he "gave me the finger." He directly and curtly told me to get my head in the match, as he poked me in the sternum with his right index finger. As I recall, this was the only time coach "gave me the finger." Everyone that wrestled for Coach Ken Larson understood the finger. It meant Coach was very upset with the way you were wrestling and expected more from you.

In overtime, I manhandled Bobby to move on to the semifinals. When we shook hands at the end of the match, Bobby was exhausted and gasped, "Skip, you're in really good shape, aren't you?" I smiled and responded, "Yeah, I am." Thanks, Coach. I needed that.

Coach Gregerson, Coach Larson, and Dr. Mike Perry all knew, in their own way, how to push me when I needed it. Dr. Perry masterfully made me address my negative thinking and to brainstorm ways to counter the mental sinkholes I fell into. He helped me determine one activity to concentrate on each week and to track it until my next appointment. Time and time again we also discussed ways to improve my insomnia. Thanks, Coach. I needed that.

The best coaches also have their wrestlers' best interest at heart. Wrestlers who know this about their coaches trust them and respond to their correction without grumbling or second-guessing them. I intuitively knew this about my coaches in junior high and senior high school. This freed me to push myself in practice, listen intently to their feedback, and to push myself to wrestle my very best in matches. Likewise, the mutual respect and trust Dr. Perry and I shared, in addition to our common faith, forged a powerful bond between us. I trusted Mike and I knew, without a doubt, he had my best interest at heart. I was committed to make the most of my weekly appointments and to follow his recommendations wholeheartedly.

Coaches teach us how to coach fellow teammates. They push us to master the basics and drill situations to prepare us for common wrestling situations and scenarios, such as losing or leading by one or two points at the end of a match, and having to score or defend, respectively, to win. They also promote their wrestlers to cheer for teammates, encourage them, and to help them to warm-up by drilling before a match. With practice, and over time, we learned to coach our teammates. My two best high school wrestling buddies, Charlie Nicholls and Russ Waag, and I, coached, encouraged and warmed up together before matches during the Freestyle Wrestling season in the spring and summer. We were not only devoted teammates, but grew to be close friends and confidantes. We coached each other during some exciting wins and some hard-fought losses. We are still close friends to this day. Thanks, Charlie and Russ. I needed that.

Another job of a coach is to teach his wrestlers to self-coach. They teach them to learn to "trouble-shoot" during a match, to become an observer-participant. This enables a wrestler to make important corrections mid-match and to learn to bounce back after a mistake during a match. It also is a critical skill after a heart-breaking loss. Every competitor must learn to bounce back. I believe it was this type of self-coaching that enabled me to come from behind to tie the quarterfinal match of the 1973 Colorado State Wrestling Tournament, regroup, and then dominate Bobby Lucero in overtime. Thanks, Coach. I needed that.

Dr. Perry also encouraged me to practice mindfulness to help calm my anxiety, focus on the moment, and improve my clarity of purpose. The practice of mindfulness is an exercise as an observer-participant. Initial attempts at mindfulness were difficult. My mind raced and jumped from one thought to another. As I shared earlier in the book, fearful, doubtful, and unhelpful thoughts ran through my mind day and night.

Becoming more mindful of my thoughts and their effect on my emotions was important to my recovery. I needed to recognize, acknowledge, and dispassionately examine the validity of my thoughts. I had to "drill" the practice of mindfulness over and over in multiple situations and at various times, to become more effective in self-coaching. Dr. Perry encouraged me in my attempts, celebrated successes, and provided insight in how to do this more effectively. Thanks, Coach. I needed that.

The best coaches walk alongside their wrestlers because they have been in the same situations. With few exceptions, they also were wrestlers. It is, in part, this shared brotherhood of wrestling that helps forge a bond of mutual respect between coach and competitors. Likewise, the formation of a therapeutic bond, a mutual trust and respect, is crucial in the practice of any of the disciplines of medicine. This is perhaps even more true in the relationships between patients with depression and other mental illnesses, and their counselors. Once a therapeutic bond is formed, sufferers heal and recover faster, and without it, they recover more slowly.

Wrestlers sense this bond of mutual respect and trust at a visceral level, respond positively, and, as a result, are more coachable. Coaches learn to use this to their advantage when they must discipline, correct, or bolster the confidence of their wrestlers. Shared experiences, especially difficult ones, contribute to this powerful bond. During my depression, my mom and my brother Chris most closely identified with me because of their own experiences, and that of other members of their families.

They understood what it was to struggle with this dark disease, and as a result we forged that same kind of bond.

In May, 2016, my buddy Russ Waag and I reminisced, over lunch, about an invitational tournament before Christmas Break of our Junior Year. It had been almost forty-four years and we still relished the memories of this win. The sense of satisfaction and pride we shared with that win was a milestone in our team's journey to the state tournament. Russ said, "I can still remember the Grand Junction coach standing in the gym looking out a window and shaking his head." A month earlier, Grand Junction won the Wheat Ridge High School Invitational Wrestling Tournament, and we did not place as team. Defeating the Grand Junction High School Wrestling Team bolstered our confidence in ourselves, each other, and our coaches. We lost some early matches, regrouped, and won in a dramatic fashion. Our heavyweight, John Stephan pinned Grand Junction's heavyweight to move us past Grand Junction to win the tournament. Every wrestler won matches in the latter rounds to contribute to our point total. It was a true team effort. This experience helped forge an even stronger bond amongst our team and coaches.

Each of us faces adversity as we go through life. We can use the challenges in life to improve our resilience and to benefit others. Earlier I shared how changing my mindset from one of seeking "deliverance" from my depression, to asking how I might use my experience to serve others and honor God, was a major turning point in my recovery from depression. Thanks, God. I needed that.

Important Keys to Finding and Working with Therapists and Other Coaches

1. Committed therapists take time to get to know you, familiarize themselves with your background and symptoms, and build trust. They have your best interest at heart and can communicate this in both spoken and unspoken ways. Trust is essential to form a therapeutic relationship. Ask your doctor, pastor, trusted colleagues, or a family member or friend who have recovered from depression for recommendations for therapists.
2. It takes time to develop trust and mutual respect. Open your heart and mind. Listen to recommendations and accept those that resonate with you. If you have serious resistance to a recommendation this may prove to be fertile ground to explore the reasons for this resistance. A skillful therapist is likely to recognize this resistance long before you do. He will address it when he senses it is time to do so in order to move you forward in your recovery. This process may be painful. Having trust in your therapist will help you to push yourself past your pain.
3. Trusted coaches bring out the best from us. They stress the basics and help us to practice and work to master the basics. Dr. Perry helped me to recognize, acknowledge, and address my negative thoughts. My commitment to an ongoing practice helped me to overcome these detrimental cogitations. I was determined to "improve

my performance" to aid in my recovery. I not only wanted to regain my health and well-being, but I was determined not to let my wife, family, and my coach, Lieutenant Colonel Mike Perry, down.

4. Fellow teammates, those who have successfully contended alongside you against the common companions of depression-despair, discouragement, and defeat, can help coach you as you recover. They can be some of your most ardent and faithful supporters and encouragers. They also may become lifelong friends.
5. Learn to self-coach. It takes mindfulness to become an observer-participant to assess your thoughts and their effect on your mood and actions. If you work closely with a trusted therapist and practice the exercises they prescribe, albeit awkwardly at first, you can learn this behavior and it will become another important skill to assist in your recovery.

"Thanks, Coach, I needed that!"

Lessons Learned

- Wise coaches get to know us, earn our trust, and push us beyond our perceived limits.
- Wise and loving coaches have our best interest at heart.
- Wise and loving coaches recognize when we are struggling and come alongside us in our suffering.
- Coaches can be licensed therapists, pastors, teachers, family, or friends.

- Wise and loving coaches will challenge our wrong thinking.
- Wise and loving coaches will help us devise a plan to attack negative ruminations leading to undesirable or harmful behavior.
- Coaches rejoice in our success and commiserate in our failure and loss.
- Wise and loving coaches never give up on us.
- Wise and loving coaches forge powerful and lasting bonds with us.

CHAPTER 13

The Power of Your Team: Faith, Family, and Friends

Faith in your teammates and coaches helps sustain you during difficult losses and disappointments, and encourages you to give your very best every match. It also fuels you to push yourself in practice to improve yourself and your teammates. My high school partner, Russ Waag, and I brought out the best in each other. We had distinctive styles. I had the advantage when we wrestled on our feet, working to secure a takedown. A takedown is when you take your opponent from his feet to the mat in a controlled manner that puts you in the dominant position to work to expose your opponent's back.

Russ, however, was better when we went to the mat. He was more accomplished at reversing me, securing the dominant position if I won a takedown, or reversing me if I started in the top (dominant) position at the start of a period. Russ was especially good at controlling me once he was in the top position. If I could escape from him, we resumed wrestling on our feet, which gave me a slight advantage. This was our strategy during practice. I sought to take Russ down and escape from him as fast as possible and he worked to exploit his advantage to control me down on the mat to expose my back. We wrestled hard to impose our will on each other. Sometimes I scored more, and other times he did. Something, alas, happened halfway through our senior year. Russ sustained injuries and could no longer compete. My workout buddy was no longer in the wrestling room to push me.

I dominated the underclassmen in the wrestling room, including those 3–4 weights above me. I had to find innovative ways to motivate myself in practice. Not only did I miss the hard-fought training that Russ and I enjoyed, but the luster of victory was dimmed. To make matters worse, Charlie Nichols, my other closest wrestling friend and teammate was also injured and unable to compete. Charlie, Russ, and I had trained together since the summer of 1970. We were co-captains and among a handful of seniors on the team. We worked hard, dreamed, and expected to be wrestling alongside each other in the Finals of the 1973 Colorado State Wrestling Tournament.

It was not to be. I was the only one who wrestled in the Finals. I had some very talented and committed teammates, but I missed the special bond I enjoyed with Russ and Charlie. We shared a powerful faith in each other. We sacrificed countless hours and other activities to train and to compete, not only during the regular wrestling season, but during the spring and summer. We enjoyed traveling to tournaments together and we were each other's most ardent fans. When

Matt Martinez defeated me by a score of 2–to–1 in the state finals my buddies were not on hand to comfort me. Moreover, I grieved that they were not able to compete on that Saturday night in February 1973.

My best wrestling buddies. January 8, 1973. Skip, 112 lbs. (left), Charlie Nicholls, 145 lbs. (middle), and Russ Waag, 119 lbs. (right). We had our focus and dreams set on the State Championship Tournament. We remain close friends to this day and I count Charlie and Russ as my brothers in Christ. (permission granted by Mrs. F.W. Worthen)

My coaches had faith in me. They knew that I was always going to push myself and my teammates, and lead by example. They believed I was committed to performing my best. This helped sustain me in the latter part of the season. I needed the assurance of their quiet and implicit confidence in me. I was the most dominant wrestler in the practice room without Russ and Charlie and the *de facto* team leader.

I also had an internal drive, a faith that my training, dedication, determination, coupled with sound coaching, that I would stand on the podium as a state champion. As I mentioned in a previous chapter, it took over a decade to recover from that stinging 2–1 defeat to Matt Martinez and not feel like a failure. As the years pass, I continue to have an ever-growing appreciation for the faith of "my wrestling family" and their encouragement and support during my high school career. Faith: without it, it's hard, perhaps impossible, to sustain the battle, in the face of discouragement, despair, and defeat.

In the darkest of days when I wrestled with depression I drew from the deep wells of my faith in God, wells dug over the previous forty-two years. My faith had to sustain me when God seemed distant and quiet in the midst of my suffering. I wondered why I could not "hear" His voice and agonized that I could not sense His presence. Yet, on another level I sensed He was closer than the cries of my heart and understood my anguish and tears. I attempted to pray, read and study my Bible. Yet, I was attacked by fear, doubt, self-incriminating ruminations, and the inability to focus and recall what I read or retrieve what I previously learned. Regular attendance at church services was a must. Before I sought treatment for my depression, I fretted that others at church would notice my trembling hands and quivering voice during singing, along with a departure from my normal optimistic demeanor. Once diagnosed, I was more open to share my struggle and to receive the care and nurture from my church family. I also enlisted the prayers of family and friends.

As I said previously, some days I felt like I was holding on by my fingernails. Through tears, doubts, and fears, I refused to give up. I clung to the glimmer of hope that God had not given up on me. My faith in God is an integral part of my life. Although severely tested, faith has given me, and continues to give me, peace, purpose, and "power" to endure pain and loss. Have you considered the faith God and others have in you, and vice-versa?

Dr. Dale A. Matthews, MD, has spent his career studying the scientific evidence of the faith and prayer related to healing. There is a mountain of evidence that supports the positive effects of prayer and faith in God to promote healing, health, and well-being. In his book, *The Faith Factor: Proof of the Healing Power of Prayer*, Dr. Mathews summarizes many of his findings. Faith in God and the prayer it engendered were critical elements to my recovery. It was also my faith that led to my "epiphany" to see my suffering as redemptive.

This epiphany led to a paradigm shift in my heart and mind. This shift, you may recall, in my mentality, attitude, and outlook was pivotal in my recovery. I stopped pleading, "Lord, please deliver me from this horrible darkness." Instead, I prayed, "Lord, what would you have me to learn and how can I use it to help others?"

My focus shifted from me, to God, and then to others. Depression drew me inward, isolated me, and insulated me from the warmth, comfort, and kindness of God and others. Faith and prayer were critical to help me open my heart, mind, and life to receive love, comfort, and healing.

My family was also instrumental in my healing. They never lost faith in me. They called, wrote, and prayed. They offered encouragement and support. My most faithful supporter is my wife, who has loyally stood at my side since we stood at the marriage altar in 1981. My sweetheart understood she could not sink into the darkness, despair, and despondency I experienced. Instead, she stood at the rim of the pit and with resolute compassion, kindness, and determination, lent her support, encouragement, and faith.

I have long realized that Sherry is an amazing woman. I was drawn to her because of her sincere faith in God, love and appreciation for family, and her bright and discerning mind. Her unwavering love, support, and encouragement during my darkness provided glimmers of hope to help sustain me. Yes, Sherry has always been my #1 fan! Just as I have been hers!

I also belong to an exceptional family. I am the third of eight children. I was surrounded by the love and encouragement of my maternal grandmother, Audelia Anaya, my mom, Esther Luben, and my stepfather, my "Daddyo," Edward Luben, as I grew up. My siblings and I are exceptionally close and we all enjoy a common faith, values, and each other's company. My wife and I raised five amazing children, and our "tribe" as of this writing includes two wonderful daughters-in-law, a fine son-in-law, and four fabulous grandchildren. My siblings are all married and our clan includes scores of nephews and nieces, many of whom are also married and raising children. Over the course of my life, I've been blessed to enjoy an extensive support system. They are an incredible source of love, encouragement, and support in time of need.

My mom, or "Mother-dear" as I have dubbed her, called frequently, sometimes two or three times a week. She also prayed with and for me. She repeatedly expressed her love, concern, and resolute hope in my recovery. My brother, Chris, called regularly, texted words of encouragement, prayed with me, and was instrumental in my recovery when he shared a Biblical basis for suffering. My sister, Margo also regularly sent me uplifting cards. Other family members also called to encourage me. The loving calls, cards, and concern were lifelines that I clung to.

My children and their spouses were kind, caring, and very patient with me. They expressed their love and appreciation in special ways. One such occasion was June of 2014. We were gathered in Colorado for a nephew's wedding. They conspired to take me out a few days before Father's Day, under the guise of dinner for our immediate family. Wow, did they surprise me!

They made reservations at a Texas de Brazil Steakhouse in Denver and drove Sherry and me to the restaurant. We feasted on food, fun, and fellowship. Toward the end of the meal, four of my five children, Chris, Angeli, Jonathan, and Joey, presented me with gifts. Unfortunately, my oldest son, Adam, was not able to make the trip to Colorado. The most memorable gifts were framed acrostics. Using the titles of "PADRE," "COLONEL MONDRAGÓN," "FATHER" and "DOCTOR MONDRAGÓN," they ascribed characteristics of me to each letter. When the bill arrived and I took out my wallet, my son Chris looked at me and said, "We've got this Dad."

I was delighted, encouraged, and affirmed. I had crafted scores of acrostics for family, friends, and colleagues over the years to express my love, appreciation, and commitment to them. This was the first time I had been presented with an acrostic. I received not only one, but four. Also, almost without exception, when our family went out to eat, I've picked up the tab. Now the tables were turned. I basked in the memories of their love for weeks to come.

If not for Sherry, I would have missed this opportunity. Earlier in the year, after we received the invitation to our nephew's wedding, I sighed with regret, "I don't feel like doing anything. I don't feel like going to this wedding." Sherry encouraged me to go, saying, "If you don't go, you'll regret it." Then she proceeded to make travel plans. June of 2014, early in the course of treatment for my depression, my emotional, mental, and physical stores were tenuous. Yet, Sherry, in her wisdom and her understanding of my nature and needs, and the nurture of our family, prevailed. Recollection of this Father's Day delight continues to warm my heart. My children not only surprised me, but they gave me a priceless gift. Their thoughtfulness and affirmation of love and encouragement provided a much-needed boost to my recovery. I later told my therapist, Dr. Mike Perry, what a powerful balm this experience was to my soul.

The time with my extended family was also a balm to my weary body and soul. They expressed their love and compassion in many ways. This was also a change of roles. Over the years, I've typically served as one of the main caregivers in our family. I would reach out with calls, cards, and letters. I supported, prayed, and expressed my love. During this trip, they cared for me. On our last day in Denver, Sherry and our sizeable extended family gathered to pray for me. They anointed me with oil, laid hands on me, and offered fervent and loving prayers on my behalf.

On our return home and for days to come, I thanked Sherry for insisting we attend the wedding. My sweetheart knows me well and she understands how I treasure time with family. Without her insistence, I would have missed these gifts that money cannot buy, and once past, cannot be retrieved. Thank you, my love. I needed that.

Early on I did not broadcast my illness widely. I shared it only with our pastor, our volunteer priest, and a few trusted friends at church. They all lent their encouragement, love, and prayers. They would take me aside from time to time to inquire about my status, affirm their love and concern, and offer to pray with me. Yes, indeed, I enjoyed a powerful support system of my wife, children, extended family, and my church family.

I understand everyone does not have a devoted partner, loving family, or committed church family to lean on when they face adversity and struggles. The "family of our choice," such as close friends, can serve this role. I have a handful of close friends, including Marilynn Force and Barb Junge, dating back to September 1968 when I first attended Everitt Junior High School. Russ and Charlie from high school, and a few others, such as Paul and Kay Rasch from my undergraduate years at Oral Roberts University. These and others lent encouragement, compassion, and offered many prayers on my behalf over the years. I told my children as they grew up, "If you have a few individuals that remain friends with you over the course of your life, you will be blessed." I am truly blessed!

Over the decades, months and even years may pass between the times my friends and I get to see each other in person. Yet our commitment, concern, and care for one another endures. We enjoy and appreciate each other. We have consoled one another after severe losses and setbacks. We have laughed, cried, and reminisced together. Over time, we've forged a powerful chain of friendship. Thanks, my friends.

Lessons Learned

- Faith in God can sustain you when you are at the end of your rope.
- Faith can provide comfort, hope, and strength. If you don't belong to a faith tradition or engage in one, I encourage you to explore a relationship with God.
- Evidence abounds that prayer and faith in God are powerful "medicine" to help in the recovery from illness.

- Faith in God can also provide you with a paradigm to better understand suffering and how it can be redemptive in your life and the lives of others.
    - It can help you, as it did me, to move from a "me-focus," to a "God-focus," and ultimately to an "other-focus."
    - Faith helped me break free from the power of the lonely inward, isolated, and insulated effects of depression.
- The faith, love, and encouragement of a committed partner can provide a healing balm to your anguished soul.
- The importance of having a number one fan in your corner "yelling" words of encouragement cannot be overstated.
- Your immediate and extended family can also provide an invaluable source of strength, encouragement, and support when your faith, health, and well-being are tenuous.
    - Lean on them and cherish their loving words and kind and thoughtful actions.
    - A loving and supportive church family is another valuable source of support and love.
    - Their faith can bolster you when yours is flagging.
    - If you do not belong to a church or faith group, I encourage you to visit one.
- Faithful, trusted, and loving friends can provide an additional source of encouragement and strength.

- If you lack a loving partner, family, and church or faith family, you will find love, support, and encouragement from the friends you lean upon most heavily.
- Building a team of support that includes your faith in God, your spouse or partner, your family, and your friends will provide you with several layers of love, encouragement, and accountability.
    - This team can provide a significant boost to help you grapple with and break free from the powerful grip of depression.
    - This team can also bolster your resolve as you contend to reverse the negative effects of depression during your recovery.

CHAPTER 14

Get in the Zone

Earlier, I described the importance of the mental aspects of wrestling and how essential this was to improve my performance. Sports psychologists refer to the ability of high-level athletes to optimize their performance when they're "in the zone." This has also been described as "being in the moment," and "performing instinctively." This mental state is not just the province of athletes, but musicians, actors, and writers. My wife, Sherry, is a writer and lights up after a good writing session, saying, "It's like stepping into the river and letting the current move me."

I recall a match when I was "in the zone." In a dual meet during my sophomore year of high school we wrestled against a neighboring Jefferson County team, Alameda High School. My buddy, Russ, defeated his foe at 98 pounds and our 105-pound teammate also won a close, hard-fought match. I was up next. I don't remember much about my match—except shaking my opponent's hand before the match, that it was a high scoring match, and that my opponent shook his head in puzzlement and surprise as we shook hands after the match, just before the referee raised his hand in victory.

As I walked off the mat, my coaches asked me if I knew who I just wrestled. I shrugged and said, "No." My coaches later told me I had wrestled a great match against the number-one ranked wrestler at 112 pounds in the Colorado AAA Division. They explained that my opponent, John Meyers was the runner-up at 98 pounds from the 1970 Colorado State Wrestling Tournament. I wrestled that match "in the zone" and pushed him. I was an unknown and unheralded sophomore. I hadn't beaten anyone of repute in our weight class. Yet, I managed to successfully execute several moves against him, to the surprise of my teammates and coaches, his team and coaches, and the fans in the gym familiar with his credentials. Alas, this was not the case when I faced him at the Jefferson County Tournament.

The top two wrestlers of the County Tournament qualified for the State Tournament. We met in the second round of the Jefferson County Tournament and he destroyed me. I spent most of the match fighting off my back. I managed not to get pinned, but not much more. Ugh, not one of my shining moments. It intrigues me that I remember far more about this second match—when I wasn't in the zone.

Prior to succumbing to depression, I had begun to explore the practice of mindfulness. I practiced becoming more attuned to the moment, my mindset, emotions, bodily sensations, and surroundings. I found slowing my mind and body down enough to "listen" to what I was thinking, feeling, my bodily sensations, and my environment hard to achieve. Yet, I made some progress.

Eight months before my diagnosis, I began to meet with a clinical psychologist who worked with active duty soldiers to enhance their resilience. She agreed to work with me to address my disrupted sleep. We explored my understanding of body-mind connections and ways I might use these connections to my advantage. Under her tutelage, I practiced deep diaphragmatic breaths, progressive muscle relaxation, relaxing combined with soothing imagery, and guided meditations. I made progress, but as my depression deepened, I found it increasingly difficult to relax. Once my depression was full-blown, I found it almost impossible to relax and practice mindfulness.

Not only did my mind jump from one thought to another, these thoughts became progressively negative. Self-disparaging, catastrophizing, and fearful thoughts grew in strength and frequency. My body responded in kind. My heart fluttered, my hands trembled, and my sleep became even more disrupted. It became a self-fulfilling prophecy. The more I feared I could not sleep the worse my sleep became. The worse my sleep, the worse I felt physically, emotionally, and mentally. The worse I felt, the more I worried. The more I worried, the worse I slept. This cycle repeated itself as I sank deeper and deeper into the depths of depression.

Attempts to practice contemplative prayer or to meditate were frustrated by intrusive dark and despairing thoughts and the accompanying negative bodily sensations. Only after I sought help and began treatment for my depression was I able to effectively employ the healthy and restorative mind-body practices of mindfulness.

Part of the practice of mindfulness includes not trying to push negative thoughts and feelings away, but becoming aware of them, acknowledging them, and addressing them. It's simultaneously being an observer-participant and objectively exploring negative thoughts and emotions. You may recall it was that fateful day in April 2014, when I was curled up on the floor, that I was able to be an observer-participant and finally answer the question, "Skip, what are you doing?" "You're depressed, go get some help." This was the first step to my recovery. As an observer-participant, you can tell yourself in a dispassionate manner, "That's interesting. Why do I think this way?" Then you can begin to explore the validity of this thought. "Is it true? If so, what evidence backs this up?" You can go on to inquire within about the worst thing that can happen if it were true, or the best thing that can happen if it is not true. Likewise, you can explore your emotions and the things that fuel these emotions.

Deep breathing, or "centering" as it is sometimes called, is another way to help calm your mind and body. You may recall that when I incorporated this technique in conjunction with progressive muscle relaxation and imagery, I became a far more consistent and proficient wrestler. Even now, when I am feeling anxious, fearful, or stressed, I rely on deep breaths. It's simple to practice this technique. Sit up or stand up straight and tall, close your eyes and slowly inhale, filling your lower chest/upper abdomen first, pause, and then exhale slowly. Try it to a count of three seconds to inhale, pause for two to four seconds, and then exhale slowly to a count of three to five seconds. With practice, it can be relaxing, refreshing, and re-energizing. This technique can be incorporated in almost any setting—at home, during a conversation, an interview, board meeting, in the classroom, or any situation that makes you feel nervous or tense. This is among the simplest of mindful practices to incorporate into your recovery and maintain in your arsenal of weapons to maintain wellness.

As I began treatment, I noticed I could pray more easily. My mind was clearer, my body calmer, and my heart more open. Initially I felt this way for only short periods, but as my treatment progressed, my fears, anxiety, and self-deprecating thoughts became less prominent. The improvement in my clarity of mind allowed me to focus for longer periods, recall what I read in the Bible or other spiritually-related literature, and not get sidetracked so easily. Success begets success. The improved ability to pray for longer periods without my mind and heart racing, and the intrusion of fear and a sense of dread, led to an improved mood. Prayer has been a part of my life for as long as I can remember and I found it distressing not to be able to sit and quietly pray while my depression raged on.

Before I began to succumb to depression, I started to explore yoga. I found it relaxing and enjoyable. However, as my depression progressed, I stopped attending yoga classes. This was to my detriment. This mind-body practice has also found its way into the treatment of U.S. Armed Forces Service Members to help treat mood disorders, traumatic brain injuries, and chronic pain, with encouraging results among my fellow Service Members and veterans.

Imagery has been another practice I have employed over the years. Unfortunately, as with prayer, I found it very it difficult and frustrating that I could not sit quietly and enjoy an imaginary peaceful scene. Instead, negative scenes flashed through my mind and contributed to my anxiety and fear. This practice is now once again a part of my life. I especially enjoy imagining a small waterfall cascading down a beautiful forest scene with a gentle roar and enjoy the spray of cool water, sunshine, scattered clouds, and the sight and smell of moss, plants, and trees. After repeated practice, I can "go to this place" quickly and sometimes I incorporate it with prayer, or in conjunction with deep breathing and meditation.

Meditation can take many forms. Unlike some practitioners, I do not attempt to empty my mind. Instead, I seek to calm my mind and body with prayer, deep breathing, or imagery first. Once I am in a relaxed state, I give thanks for those things that readily come to mind. I proceed to examine my heart and determine if I feel hurt, disrespected, or disregarded by others. If so, I offer forgiveness. I also forgive myself and endeavor to speak kindly to myself. Remember, self-care is not selfish. I conclude by expressing gratitude and then set an intention of what I wish to accomplish and, more importantly, the person I endeavor to be.

Nature and its beauty, diversity, and wonder also provides another avenue of mindfulness. Growing up in Colorado, I enjoyed walks at twilight under clear skies and wondrous stars. Colorado's low humidity and higher altitude generally herald a quick drop in temperature, even on the hottest of days, as the sun sets. Over time these walks became a time of reflection, prayer, and, and in retrospect, meditation. I had a favorite hill that when crested, I could look out on the beautiful Denver skyline and in the other direction to the powerful and majestic mountains. Moving to other parts of the country meant I had to find other ways to commune with nature. Our last assignment in the Army was in Augusta, Georgia, where there were no nearby mountains and hot temperatures coupled with high humidity are the norm. Here I found new wonders to enjoy and new ways to find restoration from God's creation.

I enjoyed sitting out on our backyard deck, basking in the sun, and marveling at the clouds, the sounds and sights of birds and flowers, and the swaying and rustling of tall pine and oak trees. When twilight approached, I marveled at how quiet and calm everything became with the setting sun. Sitting on our backyard deck became a refuge for me. On occasion, Sherry and I would sit out there and eat a meal, or enjoy a cup of coffee, the sounds, sights, and smells of our little part of nature, and one another's company. Alas, this practice ceased when I was depressed. Only after I began to recover, did I understand I had also isolated myself from the healing balm of nature.

I experienced the profound restorative power of nature in June of 2014. During our stay in Denver, my brother Duke, and his wife, Rosie, arranged to take Sherry and me to the mountains. I hadn't been in the Colorado Rocky Mountains for a few years. We drove past beautiful vistas as we climbed into the mountains. We stopped and hiked for thirty minutes to a bluff looking out onto mountain range after mountain range.

The smell of pine trees, the distinct sound of wind whistling through their branches and my hair, with sunny skies, scattered clouds, and a comfortable temperature made for an idyllic setting. I stood on that bluff for several minutes with my eyes closed enjoying the sounds, smells, and sensations. Wow, this truly was a mountaintop experience! This was just one of the experiences, on a trip I was initially hesitant to make, that boosted my recovery.

Over the years, I have marveled at mountains, deserts, forests, beaches, lakes, rivers, and oceans. All have their own distinct beauty and grandeur. Whether you stand on a mountaintop, lie on a beach, or sit with your feet in a cold stream on a sweltering day, look for the beauty and enjoy and bask in the restoration that nature offers you.

Mindfulness can take place when you interact with others. Remaining fully engaged and listening intently, or with "your eyes, ears, and heart," as I like to say, is a rare gift. The ability to slow down, turn off the to-do list, and resist the temptation to formulate an answer prior to your counterpart's completion of their thoughts takes considerable practice and self-awareness. Yet, it can add meaning and enjoyment to your life. My wife, Sherry is quite accomplished at this. She will intently interact with others and come away knowing their history, most concerning problems, and their hopes and dreams. I am dumbfounded by her ability to engender such a level of trust that others readily confide in her. I too, have experienced this, from time to time, and treasure such occasions.

Mindfulness when you eat and drink can also provide pleasure and improve the quality of your life. Instead of gobbling your food and gulping your drink, take time to savor it. Enjoy the sight and smell even before taking a bite or drink. Then with rapt attention and intention, enjoy its taste, texture, and temperature. Mindful eating has the added benefit of helping you to better sense when you are satiated, so you are likely to eat less. Consider a hot cup of coffee or another hot drink of your choice. Imagine its amazing aroma, the warmth of a hot cup in your hands, and the distinct taste and warming effect as you drink it. Yes, opportunities to practice mindfulness abound, if you look for them.

You may want to experiment with different ways to practice mindfulness, to see what resonates with you. Some techniques such as deep diaphragmatic breaths, contemplative prayer, or meditation, are meant to calm, "center," and refocus us on what's most important in life. These techniques can draw us closer to God and to our fellow human beings. Moreover, they promote gratitude and forgiveness of others and ourselves. Communing with nature allows its grandeur, diversity, and healing balm to renew us. Likewise, when we interact with others with rapt attention and intention, it helps us to rejoice with overflowing gratitude; and it reminds us we have been given the gift of life to use our time, treasure, and talents to honor God, love others, and serve others as best we can. Life is a gift.

Lessons Learned

- Don't try to disregard or push away negative thoughts and emotions.
- Instead, allow yourself to be aware of them, acknowledge them, and then deal with and dispose of them.
    - Explore them with the detached curiosity of a scientist, engaged as an observer-participant.
- Deep, slow, diaphragmatic breaths are one of the easiest ways to begin to practice mindfulness.
    - This technique can be used in private, in public, and even in professional settings.
    - A few breaths can help to calm your mind and body, to think more clearly and quickly, and to engage your creativity more fully.
    - Stop, close your eyes, and take a few deep, stress-reducing, and refreshing breaths right now.
- Deep breathing lends itself to incorporate with other mindful practices.
- Yoga has been shown to improve mood disorders, traumatic brain injuries, and chronic pain.
    - It is best to find an experienced teacher who can help you learn the basics and to guide you in ways to adapt poses based on your level of fitness and physical limitations.
    - Many gyms, YMCAs, and Senior Centers offer yoga classes.

    - The interaction with others may also prove beneficial to your mood.
- Prayer has been a mainstay of mindfulness for millennia.
- There are many ways to pray and prayer lends itself to almost any situation.
    - Prayer does not require inordinate amounts of time.
    - Because of the difficulty of remaining calm and focused for any duration when you are depressed, I recommend you only start with a few minutes a day.
    - As with other mindful practices, don't allow prayer to be another source of frustration.
- Meditation is another mindful practice that can be either be employed separately or in conjunction with other practices.
    - Start with a few minutes and don't be discouraged if you cannot seem to quiet your mind and body.
- Imagery is a powerful tool and its healing and calming effects can be multiplied when used with deep breathing, progressive muscle relaxation, or meditation or prayer.
- Nature provides a healing touch to the weary mind, body, and heart.
    - If you've disengaged yourself from nature, as I did, look for a way to re-engage.
- Make yourself fully available to the person in front of you.
    - Practice listening with your eyes, ears, and heart.

- Savor your food and drink.
  - Make sure you consume brain-enhancing, body-enhancing, and mood-enhancing nourishment.
- Don't be overwhelmed by the various mindful practices!
  - If you are a novice you can easily combine the benefits of nature, deep breathing, and prayer or meditation, starting with a few minutes a day.

CHAPTER 15

Enjoy the Journey

My brother Chris and I enjoy talking about wrestling—matches we competed in, matches we watched, and how we trained to compete effectively. On separate occasions, my brother Chris has said, "Training for wrestling is lonely." The first time he said this I pondered it and then inquired, "What do you mean?" He went on to explain that most of our conditioning and much of our off-season training was done alone. As I considered his words, I pictured all the training I did on my own: waking up early to go for a run; regular sessions in the weight room; countless push-ups, sit-ups, and chin-ups; hours spent with a jump rope; stretching and agility drills; and, simulating moves with an imaginary opponent. Chris enjoyed far more success, wrestled in far more matches and tournaments, and wrestled on bigger stages than I, so he spent even more time training alone.

After the 1974–75 wrestling season, my sophomore year at the University of Notre Dame, I realized I could not effectively juggle the demands of college wrestling and college academics. My performance in both was subpar and this left me very frustrated. Something had to give. The heart-wrenching decision to discontinue college wrestling ensued. My brother Chris, however, attended North Carolina State on a wrestling scholarship. He had to learn to juggle the demands of college coursework and competition at the Division 1 level. Although he was surrounded by other Division 1 athletes, most of his training, apart from scheduled wrestling practices, was done on his own. Yes, training for wrestling is a lonely affair.

A different class schedule, different priorities, and different level of commitment than his teammates meant that Chris trained on his own. Chris and I understand that to sustain the motivation to push yourself physically, mentally, and emotionally, day in and day out, you must learn to love the journey. You must learn to find joy in the process and ways to celebrate along the journey. You learn to relish a fast run time or a new chin-up record. You learn to take pleasure in the ability of your body to run on a dreary, frigid winter morning or on a refreshing and colorful fall day. You celebrate your commitment to spend time in the weight room or improving your foot speed and agility with a jump rope. You acknowledge, accept, and access a newfound sense of accomplishment after an especially demanding workout. If you don't learn to love the journey, you are not likely to endure the rigors of wrestling required to compete at a high level for any period of time.

As I began to recover from my depression, I had to learn how to once again enjoy the journey. I learned some important lessons along the way. One important lesson was to revise my paradigm of success. I am a very competitive person, not only with others, but especially with myself. I had to learn to give myself a break—not a straightforward process for an over-achiever!

In part, I learned to redefine success by different measures. I came to understand the difference between *process* goals and *progress* goals. For example, a process goal might be, "I exercised most days of the week," and a progress goal might be, "I averaged over 12,000 steps daily this week." This was especially important in the early months of my recovery. I came to understand that I spent most of my life working to accomplish progress goals. In doing so, I realized that I inadvertently put extra, unneeded stress on myself to the detriment of my health and well-being. I certainly did not need to add to my stress. I learned to listen more intently to my body. If I was tired, I modified my routine. I stopped approaching my workouts as a competition and came to look upon them as ways to decrease my stress, enhance my sense of well-being, and renew my energy.

I also gave more attention to mindfulness throughout the course of my day. I gave myself permission to celebrate and relish small successes. This required me to slow down enough to be aware of small successes. When I read material and readily recalled it, I offered up quick thanks for a clear mind. The day I stopped in the Infusion Center after a several months' hiatus, to chat with, encourage, and pray with cancer patients, was a landmark day. My heart overflowed with joy, gratitude, and humility, following this visit. I recounted this experience with Sherry over dinner that night, reliving the joy I felt. Celebrating with someone you love makes the journey all the sweeter. It is essential that you recognize, acknowledge, and celebrate process goals and small successes. Remember, "Nothing begets success, like success!" Writing these words chokes me up and brings tears to my eyes because I understand even better now what a milestone that visit was. Thank you, God. I needed that.

Another lesson I learned was to give myself permission to say, "No." I wrote early in this book that I have always served in the role of caretaker. I am hard-wired to take care of others. I have been prone to take on greater responsibility to pick up the slack of others. For example, if one of my fellow doctors had a conflict in their schedule, I was usually the first one to volunteer to take call for them. In retrospect, I came to understand that this tendency to quickly volunteer or to pick up the slack was to my own detriment and to that of my family.

I had to learn not only to say "no," but to not feel guilty about saying it. Because of this propensity to put others before myself, I had to learn to be more aware of my other commitments, priorities, and my level of emotional, mental, and physical energy. Recovering from depression requires lots of energy on all levels—emotionally, mentally, and physically. It takes practice to learn to say no. It also required I rewire my thought patterns to avoid repeated ruminations and second-guessing about whether I was right to say no in the first place. My wife was very helpful during this stage of my recovery, reminding me that I needed take care of myself first, and that it was okay to do so. Saying no doesn't require me to feel guilty or to give an explanation; I can simply say "No." So can you. Stop right now and state, "I can say, 'No!'" Remember, self-care is not selfish.

Learning the lesson of "no" allowed me to focus more of my emotional, physical, and mental energy on my recovery. It took time to replenish my stores and to rebuild my resiliency. Saying no to responsibilities that were not mine also freed me to focus more on the priorities in my life. It gave me more time, energy, and space to cultivate my relationship with God, my wife, and my children and grandchildren—a good trade-off. Investing your energy and time for what's most important in your life can pay powerful dividends in your recovery and its maintenance.

Freeing up time, energy, and space also allowed me to pursue long-held interests that I had largely put on hold. For example, for many years I've been fascinated by great communicators. President Lincoln's Gettysburg Address, delivered in somber tones to commemorate one of America's bloodiest battles, is touted as one of the greatest speeches in our Nation's history. The legendary speech of Prime Minister Churchill to the House of Commons and people of the United Kingdom, promising only "blood, toil, tears, and sweat," bolstered the U.K. to resist the Axis Powers. Martin Luther King, Jr. inspired a sprawling crowd in the shadow of the Lincoln Memorial in 1963, and influenced generations since by proclaiming, "I have a dream…." Great orators such as these famous men inspired me to pursue public speaking. So, in January 2015, I joined Toastmasters International to improve my public speaking. Opportunities for public speaking have provided me immense pleasure, satisfaction, and a platform to encourage others.

In September 2014, I addressed a large crowd of Soldiers and civilians working at Eisenhower Army Medical Center in Augusta Georgia. I chose to share my decline into depression, the myriad of symptoms associated with depression, and to encourage those present to seek help if they were dealing with similar symptoms. Most of this talk revolved around lessons learned during my illness and recovery. This was a small contribution to decrease the stigma of depression and the reluctance of sufferers to seek help.

This also spawned the idea of working with the U.S. Army to produce three different public service announcements to encourage those suffering with behavioral health issues to seek help. Other speaking opportunities have provided a venue to share my personal story and chip away at the stigma associated with depression. Consider the power of your own story of depression. You may feel reluctant to open this painful chapter in your life to others. You might consider sharing your story as a way to encourage others to seek help. It will be a balm to your soul. You may not be comfortable on a public stage, which is fine; instead, you might begin by sharing your own journey one-on-one, with family and trusted friends.

The idea of going public and sharing my story on local and Army-wide levels germinated and grew out of mindful sessions of prayer, meditation, journaling, and reflection. Likewise, these mindful practices and others can spawn ideas that will not only benefit you, but others.

Learning to say no was an important lesson for someone like myself, an avowed caretaker. Over many years, I had developed inappropriate boundaries, which predisposed me to take on responsibilities that were not mine and contributed to my mental, emotional, and physical exhaustion as I progressed into the depths of depression. Profound guilt is one of the cardinal symptoms of depression, and I had to learn how to let go of feeling guilty about saying no to others and yes to self-caregiving. During recovery, I found it to be important to be selective in the responsibilities and projects I took on, and zealous in monitoring my mental, emotional, physical, and spiritual state.

What have you wanted to do over the years, but have put off for a variety of reasons? Consider the power of "No!" Make space in your life, free energy to listen to your heart, and then give yourself permission to pursue a long-held desire. If this activity has the potential to help others, it provides an additional benefit. If not, don't feel guilty. Remember, self-care is not selfish.

Gratitude is another adjunct to your healing. Heartfelt words such as, "Thank you," or, "I appreciate your thoughtfulness," and "I am grateful for…" are a much-needed salve for the soul. Over the years, a Gratitude Journal helped change my focus. Taking time to recount blessings—instead of failures, setbacks, and negative experiences and emotions—reframed my outlook. At the end of the day, the simple practice of reflection, recollection, and recording five items that engendered thankfulness was a profound experience. Items such as a beautiful sunrise, a kind word from a colleague, or the glorious recognition of a clear mind, were all entries at one time or another.

When depression has you in its powerful grip it may be hard to see anything that engenders a grateful heart. Start giving thanks for God's love. He is closer than the cry of your heart. Give thanks for family members or friends who love you. As you open your eyes and begin to look around through a new lens you might give thanks for ample food, electricity, potable water, flushing toilets, hot showers, and a comfortable bed. Three stints in the Middle East during wartime gave me a new appreciation for electricity, a comfortable bed, and the sheer wonder and pleasure of a hot shower. During these deployments I "enjoyed" a few weeks of cold, makeshift showers every few days: a 2-liter bottle of water with holes punched in the cap. Gratitude helps change your focus, your thoughts, and your heart. What can you give thanks for right now?

If you don't slow down your pace of life, both internally and externally, you may overlook otherwise obvious blessings. In observing and talking to individuals from other countries, I have seen how they purposely live life at a slower pace than most Americans. We are preoccupied with the next meeting, appointment, or outing. We rush from one activity to another and have trouble slowing down enough to be fully present during the moment. A conscious and purposeful decision to practice "the power of presence" can bring greater joy, wonder, and refreshment into our lives. Incorporating mindful practices is a powerful way to help us slow down and smell the flowers.

The relentless pursuit to attain, accomplish, and acquire is counter-productive over time. Great wrestlers learn to be mindful, without ever calling it that. Wrestlers must learn to listen to their bodies and minds and adjust their training when they are battle-weary or injured. In the early days, my brother Chris and I learned this the hard way; we often over-trained, neglected minor injuries, and only came to understand the critical importance of rest and recovery late in our respective careers.

In life, it is important to recognize the ebb and flow of our internal resources. This has been one of the most important lessons of my recovery and maintenance of health and well-being. I am now more in tune when my internal resources need replenishment, if I slow down enough to take inventory. Sometimes this occurs during prayer, meditation, or even in a heartfelt conversation with my wife. Journaling has also been another vehicle to monitor my internal stores, share my heart, and vent anger or frustrations. Sometimes my journal is privy to thoughts and emotions that I do not want to share with others because, if expressed in person, they would be hurtful. Sometimes I lament over unthoughtful, even hateful or hurtful, things others post on Facebook, in an email, or on other social media. I have told many subordinates, medical students, and even my children that when they are angry and "responding" to a post or message, it is best to not hit "send," but leave the message overnight. The next day, ask yourself, "If I were talking to this person face-to-face, would I say this to them?" If the answer is no, I recommend they "delete the message." Believe me, I have followed my own advice numerous times. Thanks, "Coach." I needed that.

I have found that journaling is one of the best and easiest ways to practice self-care. It serves so many purposes: 1) Record dreams, aspirations, goals, and successes; 2) Celebrate successes; 3) Document thankfulness; 4) Dissect failures and setbacks and determine what can lessons can be learned and how can I benefit from this (If nothing else, to determine what led to these failures and setbacks and how can I avoid them in the future); 5) Record prayers and answers; and 6) Relive memories, both painful and joyful. (More importantly what I learned from these events, especially from the pain.) In short, a journal can be whatever you choose to make it.

Mindfulness and gratitude can help to build and maintain balance in your life. True joy, satisfaction, and connection with God, others, nature, and yourself, are born out of a life of balance. Appropriate and timely care for your body, mind, and spirit are essential ingredients to build balance. Attention to your most important relationships and cherishing the moment with those you love contribute to the meaning of your life and its significance.

On a closing note, I encourage you to remember the power of laughter. Laughter has many proven "medicinal" benefits. Laughter releases endorphins and other hormones that improve our mood, immunity, strength, endurance, and sense of well-being. Laughter decreases blood pressure and chronic pain. Laughter releases stress and helps us to cope with loss and grief. On numerous occasions, including in combat zones, after treating severely wounded Soldiers, some of whom died, a member of our team would share a silly anecdote to lighten the quiet grief and sobs. It worked. When we mixed laughter with our tears our burdens felt a bit lighter.

Psychologically, laughter makes you more appreciative and aware of the most important things in life, the things money cannot buy: relationships! Relationships with God, with others, with yourself, and with nature. Laughter helps you to slow down and savor these, give thanks for them, and heartily enjoy them. Laughter therapy has been used to help cancer patients, in some cases terminal patients recover, along with patients recovering from heart surgery and other diseases. Laughter is a powerful and often under-utilized medicine. There are even laughter therapist and leaders who combine laughter therapy with yoga, meditation, relaxation, or other mindfulness practices.

Have you heard of the "laughter clubs"? If you do some online research you will see an array of national and international laughter clubs. Practitioners of laughter not only have fun, but they reap its life-giving benefits. Remember, the powerful interaction of saying, thinking, and acting (i.e., power posing), all positive things to counteract the negative words, thoughts, and actions that accompany depression. Fake it, 'til you make it. Do it, 'til you feel it. Do it, 'til you become it! Thoughts, words, and actions have a powerful effect on our mental outlook, emotional state, and physiology, for better or for worse. Laughter is also powerful medicine.

I tend to be a very serious person. In fact, during my twenties, thirties, and even into my forties, my mother would say, "Son, you would think you were an old man." I'd shrug my shoulders and think, "Hmmm, I guess that's just who I am." I had to learn not to take myself so seriously and step back and laugh at myself from time to time. This is such great medicine. My brothers and I now howl hilariously when we gather and recount wrestling war stories. We enjoy reliving memorable trips and tournaments, "historic" wins and losses, and wrestling friends and foes, with gusto. This laughter helps take the sting out of losses and sweetens the successes and friendships we cultivated along the way.

Perhaps you need some low cost and simple ways to jump-start your own laughter. Here are a few ideas: funny movies with Jerry Lewis, Dick Van Dyke, and The Three Stooges are some of my favorites. Disney's 1959 version of *The Shaggy Dog* is always good for a hilarious evening of viewing. I can hardly contain myself every time I watch Tommy Kirk undergo the transformation into the shaggy dog while dancing. Sources of laughter abound.

Go watch young children learning to play a sport, or watch their parents. Have you ever watched a hoard of five-year-olds, all out of position on a soccer field, surrounding the ball? How about a confused youngster playing T-ball running to second or third base after hitting the ball, amid the shouts of coaches, parents, and teammates? Either group is sure to make you laugh. Watch AFV (America's Funniest Videos). Take out school yearbooks. If nothing else, the hairdos and cool duds we wore will help ignite some laughter. Pull out old photos of special occasions: births, graduations, reunions, weddings, athletic contests, award ceremonies, holidays, and everyday life. Relive the funny and joyful moments. Watch the antics of your children, grandchildren, or other family members, because they are always fodder for good laughter.

Reminisce, laugh heartily, and enjoy it all with those you love. This too, is great medicine. One of my favorite Bible verses is Proverbs 17:22. I have shared this verse over the years with family, friends, and fretful patients. I have written it thousands of times as a prescription. I tell others, "Laughter doesn't cost you anything, have any bad side effects, or have any detrimental drug-to-drug interactions." Proverbs 17:22 is on my business card, my personal stationary, business notecards, and included with my contact information of my email at work. I have found this Proverb to be true in my life and in the lives of many others. Now, readers, I share it with you:

"A merry heart doeth good like a medicine; but a broken spirit drieth up the bones."

I experienced a broken spirit when I faced the powerful and relentless foe of depression in 2014. This behemoth slammed me on my back, left me dazed, confused, and disheartened. My strength was sapped, confidence depleted, and hope ripped from my soul. I was fearful, fretful, and faced countless nights of fitful sleep. My *joie de vivre* dried up. I felt isolated from God and others, and misunderstood. My prayers seemed to bounce off the ceiling and go no farther. Guilt, shame, and self-condemnation plagued me day and night. I was anxious and felt a trembling within, and tried to conceal the noticeable tremor of my hands. I lacked the emotional energy to reach out and care for others. The inability to retain what I read, recall familiar names and medical information, caused me to fear early onset dementia. My body was weary and the aches and pains from old injuries were magnified. Old hurts, slights, injustices, and rejections were relived, and left me bitter, resentful, and struggling to forgive. Doom and gloom replaced optimism. I suffered in body, mind and spirit, and felt I was abandoned and stuck in the mire of a deep, dark pit.

Recovery was slow, halting, even painful at times, and required the help of compassionate and skillful professionals, medications, tender loving care from my wife and others, and countless prayers. It also required daily renewed efforts, however feeble at first, to embrace healthy practices for my body, mind, and spirit. I am still on this journey, and each day I awaken with a humble heart of gratitude. One of my favorite prayers, before I roll out of bed is, "This is the day the LORD has made. I will rejoice and be glad in it!" (From Psalm 118:24.)

My prayer and hope for you, my readers, is that you will persist in your quest day-by-day to overcome and vanquish the ravages of depression; and rebuild your body, mind, and spirit. May you be blessed with a clear and optimistic mind, a grateful and courageous spirit, and a vibrant and healthy body.

My struggle with and recovery from depression has become a source of growth, as I mine the treasures of that dark time. The fateful decision to accept and embrace my pain, and ask God, "What would you have me learn from this? How can I use it to help others?", became an avenue to share my story and the genesis of this book. Thank you for allowing me to share some of my story with you.

Wrestling is not for wimps! Its Spartan-like training prepares wrestlers for hand-to-hand combat fought on small "arenas," mats that are twenty-three feet or less in diameter, that leaves its combatants bruised, bloodied, and exhausted. It pushes them past perceived limits and demands all-encompassing devotion of body, mind, and spirit. Hotly contested matches often come down to what I call the "G-factor": GUTS. Guts—that inner essence deep within our core that refuses to yield and determines, "I'll do whatever it takes to win!"

Skip in the heat of battle, en route to a championship. To the victor go the spoils! 1978 Rocky Mountain AAU Open Freestyle Tournament.

I pray, my readers, you too have made this commitment, and each day will resolutely recommit yourself to regain your health and well-being. The "training" will be tough, and, at times, lonely, and even painful. Seek out your coaches, teammates, and supporters. You'll need them on this journey. Persist. Accept that there will be setbacks. Don't give up. To the victor go the spoils. Wrestling depression is not for wimps!

Lessons Learned

- When possible, choose process goals instead of progress goals.
- Pause to celebrate both small and large successes.
- Give yourself permission to say no, to preserve your physical, emotional, and mental energy.
- Say yes to those activities that energize you.
- The greatest pain in our life can promote the greatest growth and enkindle newfound service.
- Gratitude reframes our mind, heart, and life.
- Journaling is one tool for regular heartfelt reflection.
- Laughter is good medicine!

Epilogue

I have shared many tips, techniques, and tactics to arm you in your fight against depression. If you have read this book, I trust you have taken the most important step—seeking help from a trained professional. Now what? In the depths of our depression, physical, emotional, and mental energy is in short supply. This can make it hard to make many decisions. Make it easier. Just like wrestling, start with the basics. I recommend starting with strict attention to sleep. Once you feel your energy levels improve you can give attention to either diet or exercise, all the while increasing your water intake. Note, don't try to make massive changes, instead, small, successful, sustained changes over time will yield big dividends in your recovery.

As you continue to recover, look for ways to combine different techniques. For example, you might invite a close friend or your beloved to join you for a walk on a beautiful day in a park, to enjoy each other's company, laugh, reminisce, and share a healthy picnic. Drink your water and hydrate well.

Please remember, my readers and fellow "wrestlers," I was not alone in my struggle and neither are you, no matter how dark, lonely, or painful life seems at times. If you are dealing with thoughts of suicide seek help immediately. Do not delay! Go straight to the nearest E.R. Call a trusted family member, pastor, friend, coach, teacher, or neighbor, and ask them to take you to the E.R. Call 911 or the National Suicide Prevention Lifeline.

Your life matters and others care about you and love you. Most importantly, God loves you. You are one of a kind. You cannot be replaced. Suicide is not the answer. With proper treatment, TLC, time and persistence you can battle through the despair and darkness into joy and light. Like me, you too can win.

Acknowledgements

Carrie Jareed, thank you for your patience, graciousness, and persistence to assist me in this endeavor "to birth my baby." You're a gem. My amazing editor, Julie Clayton—your many insightful comments helped make this book sooo much better. I am grateful to Christine Kloser and the rest of the Capucia Publishing Team for the incredible opportunity as the awardee of the Transformational Author Contest in 2015. Writing *Wrestling Is Not For Wimps* has transformed me in ways I never imagined or expected.

I owe a deep debt of gratitude to the "A-Team," the wonderful, skilled, and compassionate health care providers who treated me during my time at Eisenhower Army Medical Center. A special thanks to Lieutenant Colonel (Retired) Michael Perry, PhD, Licensed Clinical Psychologist. Mike, you were not only my therapist, but a brother in Christ, and a friend. I salute you, my fellow veteran.

Duke, I appreciate you sharing your artistic gifts to draw the incredible and moving cover for my book. As you know, I choked up and was in tears when I opened your drawings in the mail. Ranilo Cabo, you were long-suffering, enduring twenty-plus revisions, to help fashion this cover to my specifications. Chris, "The Rookie," my alter ego: brother, you read my mind and told me, "I'll write the Foreword!" When's the next NCAA Division 1 National Wrestling Championship, National Freestyle Wrestling World Team Trials, or better yet, Freestyle Wrestling World Championships we can attend together? I love you, Duke and Chris. Little brothers, you mean more to me than words can express.

About The Author

Donald G. "Skip" Mondragón, MD, a Colorado native, is an Internal Medicine (adult medicine) specialist. He received his B.S. and M.D. degrees from Tulsa, Oklahoma's Oral Roberts University, and completed his residency in Canton, Ohio. Skip and his family proudly served twenty-six years in the U.S. Army. They were separated during four deployments for 37 months, including 30 months in combat zones.

The highlight of his military career was serving as the Officer in Charge of the 21st Combat Support Hospital, in Mosul, Iraq, from November 2003 – February 2004, during an eleven-month long deployment to Iraqi Freedom 1. He was responsible for all 220 hospital personnel, patients, and hospital operations. He also worked closely with the storied 101st Airborne Division and Major General David

Petraeus, Commander of the 101st Airborne Division, and his deputy commanders.

After retiring from the Army, Skip and the love of his life, Sherry, relocated to Midlothian, Texas. They celebrated their 38th wedding anniversary on May 30th, 2019. They are each other's #1 fan, strongest supporter, and best friend. They are the proud parents of five adult children and have four grandchildren. Skip is quick to proclaim, "May the Lord add to my tribe."

Currently, Dr. Skip is a staff doctor at the Hope Clinic in Waxahachie, Texas, a faith-based community health center caring for the medically underserved in his local county and surrounding areas.

Skip's interests include public speaking, amateur wrestling, exercising, writing, and especially spending time with family and growing the Kingdom of God.

Recommended Reading

1. Rath, Tom. *Eat, Sleep, Move: How Small Choices Lead to Big Changes.* United States: Missionday, 2013. Tom was inspired to improve his health after he lost vision in his left eye at sixteen years of age due to a rare genetic disease that caused a tumor behind his left eye and subsequent tumors throughout his body. He researched how to limit the onset and spread of these tumors and shares these lessons learned with others. He challenges readers to make small daily choices to improve the way they eat, sleep, and move to reap dividends in how they feel and function now, and to improve their health and well-being for years to come. This is an easy read, with thirty stand-alone chapters, and a First 30 Days Challenge. This small, but dynamic book contains over 400 references. If you wish to buy one book to start with, this is the one I recommend.

2. Stevenson, Shawn. *Sleep Smarter: 21 Essential Strategies to Sleep Your Way to a Better Body, Better Health, and Bigger Success.* New York: Rodale, 2016. This tome is the "Bible" on sleep. Expertly researched and clearly written by one of

the gurus of sleep, Shawn provides valuable information and practical advice. He also provides a 14-Day Plan, a Sleep Makeover, at the end of this book. Because of some of the technicalities, it may be difficult to read when you're in the throes of depression. During your recovery, this gem will serve you well, and is a must-read! Shawn's podcast, themodelhealthshow.com, is superb. He has well over 200 archived shows related to sleep, diet, exercise, emotional and relational well-being, and a variety of other topics. He features numerous top-notch experts on his show. This weekly podcast is well worth the investment in time. You can even incorporate it into your daily exercise routine.

3. Amen, Daniel G. *Magnificent Mind At Any Age: Natural Ways to Unleash Your Brain's Maximal Potential.* New York: Harmony, 2008. Dr. Amen provides valuable information to promote brain health. I recommend you skim this book to find the information most relevant to you. I especially recommend "The One-Page Miracle" to help you focus what you say, think, and do to promote health and well-being. He also provides good insights and details for killing ANTS (automatic negative thoughts).

4. Selk, Jason. *10-Minute Toughness: The Mental-Training Program for Winning Before the Game Begins.* New York: McGraw Hill, 2009. Although written for athletes, this book has application for others who want to overcome mental

barriers by teaching them to identify and use proven mental tools to focus and perform more consistently.

5. Gable, Dan, with Schulte, Scott. *A Wrestling Life: The Inspiring Stories of Dan Gable.* Iowa City: University of Iowa Press, 2015. America's most famous amateur wrestler shares stories about his youth, growing up, friends and family. Dan is a wrestler's wrestler. He shares many stories of his career that illustrate the drive, determination, and discipline that propelled him to the top as a competitor and a coach. He also gives insights into the single-minded focus, unparalleled passion, and unmatched work ethic that made him the 1972, 68-kilogram, Freestyle Wrestling Olympic Champion, a feat he accomplished without surrendering a single point throughout the Olympic Games. This book is chock-full of anecdotes that speak to the rigors, sacrifice, and toughness of wrestlers.

6. Hoebel, Brett. *The 20-Minute Body: 20 Minutes, 20 Days, 20 Inches*. New York: Harper Collins, 2015. Brett promotes fitness by addressing exercise, "clean" nutrition, and mental workouts. He outlines selection and shopping for healthy foods, food preparation, and multiple sample recipes/menus. Brett also advocates a proper mindset to promote fitness. This is a very valuable aspect of this book. The exercise routines are varied, fun, progressive, and may challenge you, if you do not have a fair level of fitness. Likewise, the food preparation may prove to be too demanding if you

are in the depths of depression. In the long run, however, the section on food can help save time, mental energy, and help you to make wiser food choices.

7. Gethen, Kris. *Body By Design*. New York: Touchstone (Simon & Schuster), 2011. Kris addresses motivation, inspiration, and especially accountability to assist you in your journey to change your lifestyle regarding diet and exercise. An overarching theme is the importance of joining a community of like-minded accountability partners, including an extensive online community, to help keep you on track. This is an example of enlisting the help of a supportive community and good teammates.

8. Phillips, Bill and the editors of Men's Health. *The Better Man Project: 2,467 Tips and Transforming Techniques That Will Flatten Your Belly, Sharpen Your Mind, and Keep You Healthy and Happy for Life!* New York: Rodale, 2015. You can pick and choose from a smorgasbord of practical tips and "factoids," from preventative health measures, a variety of exercise and diet tips, stress management, to improving your sleep, sex appeal and sexual function.

Resources

1. NIMH. National Institute for Mental Health. *https://nimh.nih.gov*

   Trusted site with extensive information, including medical articles, easy-to-read information, and links to other sites.

2. MedlinePlus. *https://medlineplus.gov*

   MedlinePlus links to NIMH and other federal government agencies, and to health information from non-government websites. Information is geared to standard sixth grade literacy level for medical information, and available in English and Spanish. Information can be accessed Under Topics, A-Z, Mental Health and Behavior, or Exercise and Fitness. This site has a treasure trove of information.

3. Mental Health.gov. *https://mentalhealth.gov*

   This site is arranged topically, has links to various other websites and services, including veterans' services.

4. NAMI. National Alliance on Mental Illness. *https://www.nami.org*

   This organization advocates for research, public policy, and promotes awareness of mental illness. Those needing help can call 800-950-NAMI, search *info@nami.org,* or text NAMI to 741741.

5. National Suicide Prevention Hotline: 800-273-8255

Please feel free to contact me at:

Webpage: www.wrestlingisnotforwimps.com
Facebook: @SkipWNW
Twitter: @SkipWNW

Made in the USA
Columbia, SC
28 February 2020

88494874R00115